THIRD EDITION

# primate
# behavior

THIRD EDITION

# primate behavior

JULIE A. TEICHROEB
*University of Toronto Scarborough*

LISA C. COREWYN
*Ithaca College*

JAMES D. PATERSON
*University of Calgary*

WAVELAND

PRESS, INC.

Long Grove, Illinois

For information about this book, contact:
Waveland Press, Inc.
4180 IL Route 83, Suite 101
Long Grove, IL  60047-9580
(847) 634-0081
info@waveland.com
www.waveland.com

**Photo credits**
**Cover**: Hendi Sujatmiko/Shutterstock; **p. 3**, Tetyana Dotsenko/Shutterstock;
**p. 11**, Carl Jones Photography/Shutterstock; **p. 33**, Jamen Percy/Shutterstock;
**p. 45**, Berendje Fotografie/Shutterstock; **p. 55**, Ondrej Prosicky/Shutterstock;
**p. 65**, Roop_Dey/Shutterstock; **p. 85**, SanderMeertinsPhotography/Shutterstock;
**p. 101**, mark higgins/Shutterstock; **p. 107**, Don Mammoser/Shutterstock;
**p. 113**, SUPREEYA-ANON/Shutterstock

Printed in the United States of America

7  6  5  4  3  2  1

*To the world's nonhuman primates,*
*who have given us so much,*
*and to the aspiring primatologists*
*who will help ensure their future*

# Contents

---

## PART TWO
### Exercises

---

# Preface

The discipline of primatology, especially primate behavioral studies, is extremely attractive to students. It promises excitement, remarkable and fascinating animals, cultural enrichment in distant locations, and, on occasion, public acclaim. We were similarly attracted to this field and are still fascinated by primate morphology, physiology, and demography, but particularly the behavior, ecology, and evolution of our nearest animal relatives. Additionally, as primate populations worldwide have become increasingly threatened with extinction, conservation science has become a critical area of inquiry for us.

Before he retired from the University of Calgary, one of Jim Paterson's goals was to pass on an enthusiasm for primates to his undergraduate students, and he hoped they would go on to their own research careers. He wrote the original edition of this text (1994) and the updated second edition (2000) to train primate behavioral ecologists. Julie and Lisa were among the many undergraduates he influenced and inspired to complete Masters and PhDs in primatology, and become professors with research programs. Jim's goal was thus achieved.

We hope that this fully updated edition of a book that was foundational to us will similarly be useful and inspirational to a new generation of students who wish to learn about nonhuman primates. Moreover, the book can serve as a resource for established primate (and other) researchers.

The primatology profession offers gratifying experiences but requires long hours of hard physical work, often under uncomfortable and sometimes dangerous conditions. Self-discipline and incremental progression are the cornerstones of success. We hope that this workbook conveys the fascination and joy inherent in scientific research while preparing students for frequent disappointments. Throughout we have emphasized accuracy, precision, and effective communication of results.

The original edition resulted from more than a half-decade of experimentation in teaching the skills and techniques of observation. The Second Edition added new concepts, including a suite of field ecology exercises. In this Third Edition, we have thoroughly updated each section and expanded the chapters on statistics, measuring social behavior, and technological applications for data collection. New chapters are provided on biological and morphological sampling, and software and methods for storing, compiling, and analyzing data.

This edition's exercises remain as they were originally, based solidly in the "scientific method" and grounded upon empiricism. However, each was updated, and new exercises were added to build students' capacity to analyze social interactions and combine data collection techniques. We have also added online resources (see the book's webpage at **waveland.com**) so students, instructors, and researchers can access practical resources to aid in their success and check for ongoing updates to text material.

We want this book to bring students into proximity with primates as subjects of observation, and to experience the realities of scientific inquiry. Even if you do not have the distinct privilege of studying primates in the wild, observing them in captivity can be equally rewarding (without some of the difficulties of field work!). If primates are not available for observation, the observational exercises can still be carried out on other available animals (e.g., squirrels, birds, dogs, cats, ungulates of domestic and wild forms) or on webcam footage from zoological facilities.

The exercises owe some of their structure to many colleagues. Among the earliest sources of improvement were Andrew Petto and Claud Bramblett. Other ideas emerged and were borrowed from Jim's discussions over the years with Francis Burton, Anthony Coelho Jr., Takamasa Koyama, Pamela Asquith, Mary Pavelka, Sue Taylor Parker, Anne Russon, and Lisa Gould. The current edition benefited from helpful advice provided by Greg Bridgett, Steig Johnson, and Amanda Melin. We are also very grateful to the team at Waveland Press, particularly Tom Curtin and Carrie Campbell, for their aid, support, and feedback. Any errors in grammar, spelling, or otherwise can only be laid at our feet.

We wish you the best as you embark on what we hope is an exciting and rewarding journey!

January 2021

Julie A. Teichroeb
Toronto, Ontario, Canada

Lisa C. Corewyn
Ithaca, New York, USA

James D. Paterson
Airdrie, Alberta, Canada

# PART ONE

## The Study
## of Behavior

# ONE

# An Introduction to the Observation of Nonhuman Primate Behavior

What is "behavior"? In a strictly technical sense, it is the actions carried out by an individual subject, and as such is a real phenomenon. However, in the common usage employed by most people and primatologists, it is the perceived and recorded "record" of those actions. Since behavior is internalized and interpreted by an observer, it is subject to errors. Such processed observations may have unforeseen consequences.

Nonhuman primates are our closest living relatives. Initially, primatologists observed their behavior to make better inferences about the behavior and social organization of our ancestors, supplementing the data available from the study of fossilized bones, tool remains, and living sites. This is still a primary goal in primatology, but research has expanded into all areas of behavioral ecology often with the goal of understanding how evolution has shaped the anatomy and natural history of a species and how current changing ecological pressures are affecting them. Broadly, questions in primatology address:

- the environment occupied by the species;
- the particular way that the species exploits its habitat;
- the social relationships and kinship among individuals;
- the social organization of groups;
- the reproductive ecology and behavior of species;
- the interactions among different groups;
- the anatomy and biomechanics of members of the species; and
- the conservation science associated with populations and species.

Note, however, that there is *no* assumption that any of our remote ancestors were much like any of the extant nonhuman primates. We have all been on separate evolutionary paths for some time. *There is* an assumption that similar problems of adaptation to a particular environment may lead to similar anatomical and behavioral solutions to those problems.

In the exercises presented in this book, students will be asked to observe the behavior and social interactions of nonhuman primates, mostly living in zoos, and to write reports about their observations. However, it is not a requirement of observational training that primates be used. A student could as easily study urban dogs, cats, squirrels, or raccoons. Any mammal is suitable, though one is cautioned against performing studies on human primates due to legal and ethical complications.

Since the adaptive requirements of surviving in a zoo are clearly different in many respects from those of living in the wild, many kinds of behavior may be affected, and behavioral patterns may be suppressed, enhanced (elevated in frequency or intensity of performance), or distorted. These factors should be remembered in studying the results of observations on captive subjects. A student who observes closely can learn much about the social behavior of these animals and consequently much about how to observe the behavior of free-living primates and other animals.

Students are often surprised at the close resemblances between some primate behavior and the behavior of humans in similar situations. (From this point on, for the sake of convenience, the use of "primate" will refer to "nonhuman primate" and serve to distinguish them from "human" primates). These similarities provide evidence that primate behavior, like primate anatomy, is derived in part from a common phylogenetic lineage.

Although we share a close evolutionary relationship with primates, one must not impute human motives, emotions, or intentions to these animals. This is called "anthropomorphism" and is an often unconscious form of bias that is associated with anthropocentrism, the perspective that places humans (*Homo sapiens*) as the central and most important organism in existence. While most anthropologists and primatologists decry the anthropomorphic and anthropocentric perspectives as unacceptable bias, a few researchers have followed the lead of Asquith (1986, 1997) in admitting a degree of anthropomorphism into their study methodology. A number of works (collected in an edited volume by Mitchell et al. 1997) have pointed out that it is impossible to totally expunge anthropomorphism from primatological study since it is a subcategory of "primatomorphism" that humans share with other primates. However, admission of anthropomorphism into data collection sets a dangerous precedent that could lead to extreme unconscious bias (Kennedy 1992).

Though it may be difficult, we should try at all times during data collection, analyses, and interpretation not to anthropomorphize. It ought to be clear after a few minutes of observation that these primates are not little humans, and that even if the action does reflect the same emotion, motive, or intention as a human might express under the same circumstances, the observer cannot know for certain. This is an important principle to keep in mind throughout all the observational exercises and in all scientific enterprise.

# A Bit of History

The observation of other animals is an ancient avocation (Loy and Peters 1991). Aristotle advocated it, and Darwin (1872) actualized such studies with his *The Expression of the Emotions in Man and Animals*. However, field observations of monkeys and apes have been conducted on an intensive and continuing scale only since 1958–59 (e.g., by Sherwood Washburn and his students, Washburn et al. 1965), although noteworthy observational works were conducted during the 1930s and 1940s: fieldwork most notably by Clarence Ray Carpenter (1934, 1940) and zoo studies by Sir Solly Zuckerman (1932). Other work particularly in psychology, on the intelligence and learning capabilities of apes, goes back to the experiments conducted by Wolfgang Köhler (1925) at the Canary Island Laboratory during the First World War. The period since 1958–59 has been characterized by a continual progression in the skill of researchers and the development of new techniques in field research. Studies on some species have now been ongoing at the same field sites for decades and have provided unparalleled data on the social systems and life history strategies of primates (Kappeler and Watts 2012).

Scientists of many disciplines have converged on the study of primate behavior: *anthropologists* seeking the nature of humans, and models for the development of human society; *psychologists* seeking the nature of thought processes, and the basics of learning; *linguists* seeking to understand the origins of language, and testing concepts of grammar; and *zoologists* challenged by the most complex of nonhuman animals. As these traditional disciplines converge, interests begin to blend and new methods and techniques emerge, resulting in even more productive field observations. This blending of concept and technique has enabled us to talk more realistically about functions and behavior in extinct primates, including our more immediate ancestors.

## The Study of Behavior

Behavior is what an animal does. That behavior is an exceedingly complicated issue and the study of behavior is similar in complexity. A succinct statement on this is the familiar quotation from Alexander (1975:77):

> The study of behavior encompasses all of the movements and sensations by which animals and men mediate their relationships with their external environments—physical, biotic, and social. No scientific field is more complex, and none is more central to human problems and aspirations.

Since it is our purpose to develop skills in the study of behavior, we need to be aware of what it is we are studying and the how and why of doing so. All ethologists (those who study behavior) and most primatologists (those who study primates) will recognize Niko Tinbergen's four questions (Table 1.1; Tinbergen 1963). These provide complementary explanations for the same behavior and are often thought of as levels of analysis. Tinbergen's four questions—ontogeny, phylogeny, mechanism, and function—can be compressed into two sets of two. One set represents the possible proximate and ultimate reasons for a particular behavior (Wilson 1975) or "how" (proximal) and "why" (ultimate) it occurs (Alcock 1989). In most cases, proximal questions are addressed at the level of individuals and individual behavior, while ultimate questions, being evolutionary, must be addressed to groups, populations, and species. The second set of questions conceptualizes the animal from either a diachronic (historical) or synchronic (static) perspective, examining whether the behavior can be explained by the current form of the species or by the sequential changes in a

**Table 1.1    Tinbergen's four questions.**

| | | Diachronic vs. Synchronic Perspective | |
| --- | --- | --- | --- |
| | | **Historical view** | **Static view** |
| **How vs. Why Questions** | **Proximate** | Ontogeny (development) | Mechanism (causation) |
| | How the organism's structures function | What is the ontogeny of the behavior? How could the behavior fit into the life history of the animal? How could it change over time? | What is the causation behind the behavior? What mechanism is leading to the presentation of the behavior? |
| | **Ultimate** | Phylogeny (evolution) | Function (adaptation) |
| | Why a species evolved the structures it has | How did the behavior evolve in the species displaying it? What is the evolutionary history of the behavior over many generations? | What is the function of the behavior? What is the adaptive value in terms of survival and reproduction in the current environment? |

species over generations (e.g., Sillen-Tullberg and Møller 1993; Di Fiore and Rendall 1994; Rendall and Di Fiore, 1995). Tinbergen's four questions serve as immediate guides toward understanding any behavior being examined.

# The Observer: Perception, Errors, and Observer Effects

The engine that drives observational study is the human observer, and any discipline that relies on human perceptions for its primary data gathering has a problem. Indeed, not just a single problem, but a complex and interacting set of problems is normally present. As we shall see in the methodology chapter (2), many forms of bias exist for the observer depending on their sex, age, and cultural background. But before these issues, there are others—ones strongly based on the biological structure of the observer.

One assumption that is misleading is that we "see" with our eyes. Unfortunately, the human optical system is less than perfect. The direct physical information of photons striking particular retinal cells is modified, smoothed, improved, and interpreted before it manifests itself in the visual centers located in the posterior aspect of the brain, as part of an image in our mind. The physical deficiencies of the optical system, its blind spots, and the neural pathways and mechanisms of vision are well beyond the intent and needs of this book; however, the fact that these exist should make any observer cautious about strongly affirming "This is what I saw!" Perception varies between individuals, and in modes of operation. Some observers may be proficient at locating animals in the forest, while others are more proficient at discerning fine-scale movements by individuals once they have been located. The innate differences between observers can be trained toward common ground, an issue that is taken up in the exercise on interobserver reliability (exercise 13).

Since we have so many internal links from incoming photons to realized image, there is an opportunity for errors to creep into our perception. One possible phenomenon is that the mind insists on seeing an arrested action as continuing; on seeing something in the "blind spot" where there are no retinal receptor cells, primarily by stretching the surrounding image to cover the "spot"; or by interpreting something as "seen" even though it is out of sight or obscured. Add to these problems the possibility that the intellectual operations of the observer may also create an "error of apprehension," i.e., seeing the actions incorrectly. Finally, the observer may incorrectly record the observation, their fingers doing one thing while the brain has commanded something else.

To further confuse the issue, we must note that the observer will also have an interactive influence on the subject. That is, the simple presence of the observer may cause changes in the behavior of the subject animal. During preliminary observations, this may be the immediate provocation of a flight response or an uneasy tolerance of the observer until they approach too closely whereupon flight takes place. In the early reports of primate field studies, it was common to find notations of the flight distances observed at first contact and the time required for the subjects to acclimate to a minimal observing distance. While these features are no longer commonplace in scientific reports (except as a question of risk perception in anthropogenically modified environments, e.g., Mikula et al. 2018), it remains true that a substantial amount of habituation time may be required to achieve regular observation of wild populations. Here, we define habituation as the process whereby animals slowly cease to react to the presence of observers.

Even once animals begin to get used to the presence of an observer, there will be variability in the amount of time it takes to habituate animals depending on the species, habitat, and even the individuals. For example, the mantled howler monkeys Lisa Corewyn studied in Costa Rica were easily habituated as the species is generally known to be reasonably tolerant of human presence, and the population already inhabited forest that had some level of human disturbance. Primate populations that live in unprotected habitats with high levels of hunting, however, will often flee at even the slightest detection of human presence. Ethically, these populations should not be habituated to humans until broader habitat protections are in place, as flight serves as their only protection. In terms of individuals, typically adult and subadult males are quickly habituated, but adult females, especially those with young infants, may take a much longer time to habituate.

The reactions of animals to observers will also vary by the location, identity, and the number of observers. As an example, the ursine colobus that Julie Teichroeb studied in Ghana could be approached to within 1 to 2 meters in areas where they were used to seeing people, but the same animals were much shyer inside the forest where people were rarely seen. Once habituated for Julie's project, the colobus could be approached closely in the forest but only by Julie and her field assistants. New people that the monkeys were not used to could not follow the monkeys closely in the forest without a few weeks of habituation. The take-home lesson from these examples is that the relationship between the observer and the observed is an interactive one, and variable in time and space. Observers may never be viewed as neutral or really ignored by the animals (Allan et al. 2020). This has an influence on the quality and quantity of data that can be collected, and to some extent is responsible for bias in the data.

## Wild, Free-Ranging, and Captive: Similarities and Differences

Behavioral studies of primates can take place in a range of different conditions. These can be grouped into three categories: the natural environment where the animals may or may not be constrained and influenced by human populations; large group enclosures where their activities are constrained by the presence of fences or moats, and the interactions with their keepers; and in typical zoo enclosures, surrounded on all sides by human fabrications, often with some simplified structures to encourage "naturalistic" behavior.

The differences between these three conditions might initially suggest that the behavior patterns of subject primates might be substantially different in each. However, to a great degree, the "form" of species-specific behaviors will be uniform in all environments, there may be minor variations on the patterns, but the main differences will be in the frequency and intensity of the acts. The general tendency in most primate species is for a change in frequency and hence the rate at which specific behaviors are performed, as the observer changes from natural to free-ranging to fully enclosed environments. The directionality of the rate change cannot be reliably predicted as there are a large number of "intervening" variables between the three states, but it has often been noted that aggression and grooming increase under captive conditions. Animals, especially those with big brains or large ranges in the wild, may also react to a zoo environment by displaying unnatural, repetitive, stereotyped behaviors. These are usually obvious to an observer and may be related to the current environment or the animal's early life experiences (Marriner and Drickamer 1994).

## Primatology and Ethics

As primatologists, and students of primatology, we have a primary ethical responsibility toward the subjects we study. For both field and captive studies, these responsibilities include ethical considerations for the following: choice of study species; choice of geographic location; the number of study subjects; the use of invasive procedures; the amount of interference with individuals, populations, and ecosystems; overall health and welfare of subjects; and conservation considerations (MacKinnon and Riley 2010). The Three Rs (replacement, reduction, refinement) were developed to minimize distress and harm on study subjects (Russell and Burch 1959). Though they were largely intended for laboratory animals, the principles to (1) replace animals with nonanimal subjects; (2) reduce the number of animals and/or samples used; and (3) refine research to minimize impact, can also apply to field studies. The policing of ethics in relation to scientific research is not a simple problem, but as students of behavior, ethical standards for all research work must be adhered to. For captive primates, manipulation of the care conditions, the enclosure size, feeding schedules, etc. can directly affect the subjects and hence require careful ethical consideration before implementation is allowed. For field studies, there are generally fewer issues associated with solely observing primates in their natural habitat; however, researchers must consider the ethical implications of habituation, field experiments if they are planned, and disease transmission on the primates, as well as our direct impacts on the local ecology in terms of waste disposal and habitat modification such as cutting and marking trails (Fedigan 2010; Riley and Bezanson 2018). Further details regarding guidelines for these and other ethical considerations can be found in the code of ethics developed by the American Society of Primatologists (ASP 2000, 2001, 2014).

For field studies, we also have ethical responsibilities that extend to the human communities we interact with and depend on in host countries where we carry out research on primate populations. It is vitally important that for all in-country field projects that we respect and consult the stakeholders that we work with, and involve them in our projects as much as possible. Riley and Bezanson (2018) outline our ethical responsibilities to local communities that include: obtaining local and government consent to conduct field studies; understanding how your research activities may be perceived by and impact the local community, economy, and intracommunity dynamics, and seeking guidance from community members that you can trust to overcome misunderstandings; and considering how research and/or conservation outcomes can affect the local community.

It remains the case that most, if not all, projects will require ethical approval by both the observer's home institution and the government of the area where the primates are to be studied. In North America, every university and research institution has an "Animal Care Committee" (ACC in Canada; IACUC, or Institutional Animal Care and Use Committee in the U.S.) of some form whose responsibility it is to oversee the implementation of the institution's ethical guidelines and to certify that all research, at all levels, is done in compliance with these guidelines. This implies that as a student conducting the exercises in this book, you would also be expected to submit your research proposals for certification. However, it may be the case that your instructor has done this for you, and the course is operating under a blanket approval.

For research conducted in habitat countries where primates reside, there is normally a governmental branch or agency that is charged with oversight of research projects undertaken within their boundaries. The forms, requirements, lead times, and fees charged are specific to each country. Anyone embarking on a field project needs to take into consideration these costs in time, money, and effort. Contact with those who have conducted research in the target country is the best source of information on the requirements and protocols. Established field stations may also be able to ease the process.

# TWO

# Methodology in Primate Observation

# The Scientific Method

Western civilization has produced two paradigms or operational procedures for learning about the universe around us: Mystic and Scientific. The mystical paradigm has flaws despite its widespread acceptance. It is not testable in any way, it relies on imperceptible and unmeasurable forces, and is most often "revealed" to the ignorant. In that sense, it relies largely on beliefs, which are taken on faith, trust, or confidence. The other, the scientific paradigm, while not perfect, is the best process yet developed to examine nature. It is a testable system, relies on perceptible and measurable forces and mechanisms, and has achieved the status of being the only accepted paradigm within the scholarly community. It relies on facts, which are known truths.

Data are (note: data are plural, and datum is singular) a collection of facts, and can be either quantitative or qualitative. Quantitative data are measurable in that they can be numerically expressed. For example, the number of grooming bouts per hour is quantitative data. Qualitative data cannot be numerically expressed, and are descriptive in nature. For example, a description of an infanticide event is qualitative data.

The current paradigm in science holds that the scientific method is a simple yet systematic process to understand phenomena: (1) A question is generated based on previous knowledge, observation, thoughts, or reading; (2) A hypothesis is generated, which is an "educated guess" as to how the situation under study operates or can be explained; (3) Predictions of results are generated from the hypothesis. For example, if our hypothesis is correct then the results from an experiment or study of this form will be $x$ and $y$; (4) We test the hypothesis by either conducting a well-designed experiment or proceeding to collect precise observational data; (5) The data collected from either the experiment or observations are analyzed to determine whether they support or contradict the predictions projected from the hypothesis. At this point, the entire scientific method of inquiry is directed toward *rejecting* or *failing to reject* a hypothesis. One can never prove a hypothesis, and; (6) Reevaluation: if the data contradict the hypothesis, the original educated guess is at least partially incorrect (one might have constructed an incorrect or defective hypothesis from the original question).

Rejection of a hypothesis is not "bad science," it is simply how science works, and rejected hypotheses may be equally as informative as those that are supported. At this stage, one of two things become necessary: replicate the experiment or observations to confirm that an experimental or observational error was not made; or revise the hypothesis and start over with a new educated guess. If the hypothesis is *not rejected*, then we can provisionally accept it, but in doing so, numerous new questions will arise. This entire process indicates that the scientific method is a repetitive cycle. This should not be construed as implying a "circular argument," but a helix of operations in which an incremental improvement in explanation is achieved with each "circuit" of the process. The process as applied to the study of behavior is diagrammed in Figure 2.1.

One important aspect of Figure 2.1 is the box representing "Preliminary Observations or Pilot Work." Throughout primatology and ethology, the costs associated with research are constantly influencing the conduct of research, and it would be ill-advised for a researcher to start with a research question,

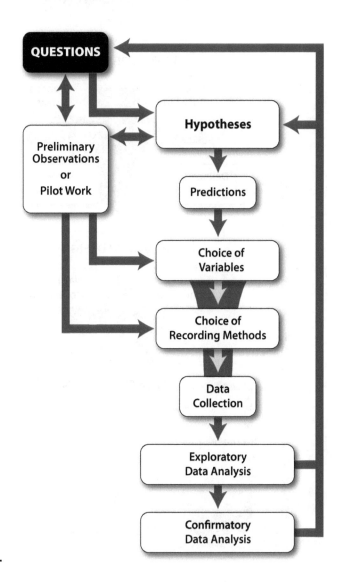

**Figure 2.1** The process of studying behavior.

sets of hypotheses, and then proceed to collect data for a long period, perhaps years, before attempting any analysis. What does the worker do if the results show that the research question or the hypotheses were inappropriate?

The safeguard against calamity is the preliminary work or test project, a trial run where the whole project design is tested, verified, and modified as needed for the testing of the hypothesis or hypotheses. This will ensure that the

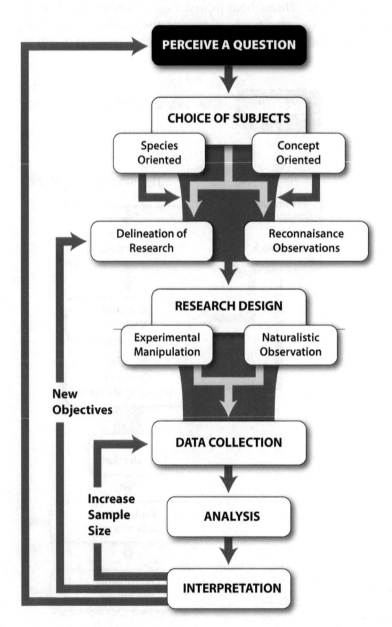

**Figure 2.2** The ethological version of the scientific method. Modified from Lehner 1996:12.

14

data being collected allows the researcher to answer the research question. It must be repeated that this process is not a correction needed to obtain "correct" results, but is one intended to make certain that the hypotheses and variables are doing what the research design intended. Of course, it is possible for this test to show that the data collection method is not appropriate or that the hypotheses are incorrect, leading the researcher to a major revision of the project. It is always better to have the project tested and verified to some degree before embarking on the fieldwork phase of the study.

Within the general field of primatology and ethology, the model can be elaborated to encompass the orientations toward particular species or concepts and the distinctions between experimental and naturalistic approaches. The discrimination between species-centered research and research that revolves around concepts or questions is straightforward (Figure 2.2). With species-centered research, the orientation is toward finding out everything possible about the subject species and draws on all questions and concepts that apply to it. With concept- or question-centered research, a particular behavior, mechanism, or model is under examination, which drives the choice of subject species. In this case, the August Krogh Principle (Krebs 1975; Lehner 1996), which states that "for a large number of problems there will be some animal of choice, or a few such animals, on which it can be conveniently studied," comes into play as a guide to the selection of an appropriate species to employ for the study (see Lehner 1996: 50–53 for a detailed description). However, this case is less important for most primatologists who are species focused or at least constrain their interests to the boundaries of the Order Primates.

## Sampling Methods and Biases

One of the most important revolutions in field primatology methods came with Jeanne Altmann's (1974) seminal paper published in the journal *Behaviour*. Altmann pointed out that the techniques of taking fieldnotes that were in use up to that time were grossly inadequate for any acceptable statistical analysis, and furthermore, that most observations were taken without any cognizance of, or correction for, biases. The biases that she pointed out were often obvious but unconsidered sources of error in "statistical" calculations presented in reports. For instance, she noted that male fieldworkers tended to overemphasize the importance of the role of the males in the social matrix of a group, and female workers did the reverse. Similarly, there was an accidental bias in that highly visible activities were more frequently recorded than were quiet, unobtrusive activities.

Also, it was evident that most workers did not take adequate care to separate two important classes of behavior—those of "states of behavior" and "events of behavior." This distinction is important because the two categories represent distinct *kinds* of data, and they must be treated statistically in different ways. A behavioral event is one that is instantaneous, momentary, of very short duration, and can be numerically expressed as a frequency or count. That is, in general terms, a behavioral event occurs in a very short period of time, and it is difficult or unsuitable to attempt to measure the duration. A behavioral state, on the other hand, is durational behavior, an activity that displays an appreciable expanse of time that can be measured. The onset of a state behavior may also be treated as an event in that each time the particular behavior occurs it may be counted for frequency. Events and states may be formally defined in this way:

- **Event:** Instantaneous or momentary behavior that occurs without measurable duration. The onset of any behavior may also be considered as an event.

- **State:** Behavior with a measurable duration (durational behavior), but may refer to any behavior at a given instant in time.

However, the distinctions are arbitrary since they depend on the capability of the observer to record the time duration involved. This limitation varies from observer to observer, and especially so when technological aids to observation are employed. It is straightforward to consider the onset of a state behavior as event, and one can refer to any behavior at a given instant in time as a state. Theoretically, if we could observe and record on a millisecond scale, we could treat all behavior as state behavior since it would be measurable in time. However, the practicalities of observational research even when using computer devices to record behavior mean that any behavior taking less than one second is recorded as an event.

Consider the following example of a partial observational record:

| Record of Observation | | Behavior Form |
|---|---|---|
| 10:32:22 | Jo-Jo receives grooming from Jay-Jay | state—134 seconds |
| 10:34:36 | Jo-Jo sits up | event |
| 10:34:37 | Jo-Jo locomotes to food dish | state—4 seconds |
| 10:34:41 | Jo-Jo eating | state—91 seconds |
| 10:36:12 | Jo-Jo drinks | event |
| 10:36:12 | Jo-Jo scratches | event |
| 10:36:13 | Jo-Jo chases Spike | state—42 seconds |
| 10:36:55 | Jo-Jo receives threat from Alice | event |
| 10:36:56 | Jo-Jo presents to Alice | event |
| 10:36:57 | Jo-Jo receives grooming from Alice | state—uncalculated |

The right column is not recorded at the time of observation but represents an after-the-fact decision tree record by the observer. This type of process is necessary to divide the behaviors into the categories of "event" and "state." Ideally, the researcher will define each behavior they intend to record as either event or state as part of the research design in an ethogram before they begin collecting data (see chapter 3 for a review of ethograms). The categorization of a particular behavior depends on two factors:

1. The actual duration of the behavior. Some activities must be recorded as events since the duration may be too short to accurately measure.

2. The arbitrary decision by the observer as to whether the recording procedure will be restricted to events only, states only, or a specific mixture of the two, with the data being separated for the analyses. In many cases, it is possible to elect to record all behaviors as events without doing injustice to the validity of the observations, however, the reverse is not true for practical reasons, and considerable distortion will result from such an attempt.

State data, since they involve durations, can be utilized to examine such things as the "time budget" of a species or population, and the proportion of time devoted to certain kinds of activity. Event data, on the other hand, provide information about rates of occurrence of those behavior categories or frequencies for a range of event occurrences. The former yields percentages of time, and the latter yields either percentages of all events or frequency rates per unit of time. It is important to recognize the distinctions between these two categories, as they will play important roles in the exercises.

In her discussion of sampling methodologies, Altmann (1974) identifies recording procedures and evaluates them as to their usefulness in producing data that are valid for statistical analyses. Many methods employed among researchers before 1974 were considered to be, in essence, useless for statistical analyses as they were largely descriptive in nature. However, a few processes were evaluated as being of limited use in particular research designs, and two—focal animal sampling, which is also known as continuous sampling, and scan sampling, also known as interval sampling—were given a general stamp of approval (see Table

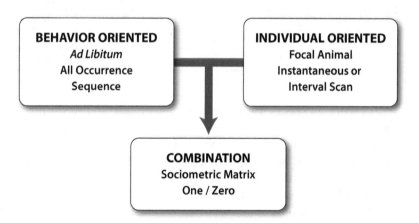

**Figure 2.3** Altmann's 1974 suggestion for Sampling Method Selection. Which methods are the most appropriate depends on whether the research is oriented toward or focused on the behavior itself or the individuals or a combination of the two, such as "adult male aggressive behavior."

2.1). In modern primatological literature, focal animal and scan sampling procedures are the predominant techniques. A subsidiary technique, focal time sampling, which might also be called "focal animal interval sampling," was developed by Baulu and Redmond (1978) and has proven to be a valid mechanism. These sampling techniques are the bases on which the observational exercises are constructed, and each is discussed further in the introductions to each method.

Altmann provides a guide to the selection of sampling methods for various kinds of projects (Figure 2.3); thus, if the project is behavior-oriented, *ad libitum*, all occurrence, and sequence sampling methods are better. If the project is individual-oriented (that is, it requires identification of individuals and keeping separate behavior records for each), the focal animal and interval (instantaneous) and scan methods are best. Only when there is a combined focus (e.g., we want to know about the grooming behavior of adult females) should the sociometric matrix, or less desirably the one/zero sampling protocol, be employed. The full set of Altmann's sampling recommendations is found in Table 2.1.

**Table 2.1   J. Altmann's recommendations for each sampling procedure (1974).**

| Method | State or Event | Recommended for: |
| --- | --- | --- |
| *Ad libitum* | Either | Heuristic value only; suggestive; rare events |
| Sociometric matrix completion | Event | Asymmetry within dyads |
| Focal animal sampling | Either | Sequential constraints; % of time; rates; durations; nearest neighbor (proximity) |
| All occurrence | Usually event | Synchrony; rates |
| Sequence sampling | Either | Sequential constraints |
| One/zero sampling | Usually state | None |
| Instantaneous and scan | State | % of time; synchrony; subgroups |

Figure 2.4 shows the separation of sampling and recording rules to clarify the process of developing a research design. The first step is the selection of a sampling rule, and while *ad libitum* and behavior sampling are available, focal or instantaneous and scan procedures are preferable. The second step is the recording rule—how the data are to be recorded—as either a continuous record or recording at intervals. If the latter is implemented (Figure 2.4), there are two methods available: instantaneous and scan sampling, and one/zero sampling. Both are similar but display distinctive characteristics. The difference is that sample point data are recorded instantaneously at the *end of an interval* for instantaneous sampling, whereas for one/zero sampling, if a behavior occurs *during the interval*, it is recorded as a "one," and if it does not occur during the interval, a record of "zero" is entered.

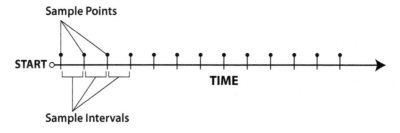

**Figure 2.4**  Relationship of sample points and sample intervals. Modified from Martin and Bateson 2007.

The sampling methods employed in any research project have a major impact on how the work will be done, and affect the validity and usefulness of the data collected. It is of critical importance that care and attention to the details of sampling be incorporated in the entire scientific process.

# Research Design

The essence of research design is potentially an extremely complicated topic on its own (see Brim and Spain [1974], Martin and Bateson [2007], or chapter 6 of Lehner [1996]). It consists of defining a problem, forming a hypothesis about that problem, devising a method of study to provide data that has the potential to reject the hypothesis, and finally the execution of the study. A "hypothesis" (plural hypotheses) is an informed explanation of a phenomenon that predicts the outcome of the research question/s you are testing. An important technical note must be placed here, and that is the explicit statement that hypotheses are always framed in pairs, null (no effect) and alternative (there will be an effect).

For example:

$H_0$: Adult females will show no preference in grooming partners.
$H_1$: Adult females will preferentially groom other adult females.

This means that in evaluating a pair of hypotheses, it should become possible to reject one of the two and to fail to reject the other. This does not mean that the alternative hypothesis is true, it has only failed to be rejected, and can be provisionally accepted, pending further testing. To avoid problems, the hypotheses being tested should be logically constructed so that there is no theoretical confusion surrounding them. Note that contrary to popular belief, the concept of "proof" cannot exist in science, only in mathematics and logic. Natural phenomena exist as open systems; they are not final. Thus, scientists use evidence, not proof, to evaluate research that may be supported, partially supported, or rejected. The ideal formation should be a logical binary "yes or no," or "it is this way or it is not this way," and if the hypothesis can be broken down to component hypotheses, then these are the ones that should be subject to testing. To conduct this testing, it is necessary to establish some relevant variables, evaluate what the variables measure, and determine how precise they are at doing so.

## Variables and Measurement

Variables and measurement constitute simplicity and inordinate complexity in the study of behavior. A *variable* is simply something that varies, in frequency, in duration, in time of occurrence, in location, with social situations, or in form of expression. Measurement mechanisms associated with these, therefore, come in a variety of forms correlated with these variables; though it is easy to set up a variable and measurement structure that will produce meaningless data. As the early computer scientists had it, there is a "GIGO" rule attached, "Garbage In, Garbage Out," and no amount of statistical juggling can turn meaningless data into useful models of behavior.

Variables fall into four distinct categories of measurement schemes, or more familiarly "scales." The scales of measurement are *nominal, ordinal, interval,* and *ratio.* It is important to be aware of the scale of measurement related to a variable as this often restricts the choices of appropriate statistical analytical techniques.

- *Nominal.* The measurement units within the variable (e.g., sex) are a set of named qualitative units sometimes conceived of as *attributes* (e.g., male or female), which can only be counted. The basic data derived from nominal level data are frequencies and relative frequencies (see chapter 6), and the statistical procedures appropriate to these data are usually limited, often to nonparametric statistical tests.

- *Ordinal.* Similar to nominal except that the categories are ranked into an ordered sequence. This ranking may relate to either a quantitative or qualitative sequencing. The distinction between the categories is not determined by a fixed distance from one to the next, but derives only from the order in that one comes before another. The scale is one of relative placement in a sequence. For example, the dominance rank of individual animals could be categorized as high-rank, mid-rank, and low-rank to make an ordinal variable.

- *Interval.* Similar to ordinal except that the categories are ranked and separated by a fixed interval along a continuous measurement scale, but there is either no zero point or it is arbitrarily assigned. As has often been pointed out, the most commonly employed temperature scales, Fahrenheit and Celsius, are interval in nature since their zero points are essentially arbitrary.

- *Ratio.* Similar to interval except that the zero point is known. Examples of familiar ratio scales are time and distance since both have a recognizable start point and display continuous interval measurement that is ordered in sequence. Ratio data are always numerical.

Studies of behavior regularly employ variables of the nominal, ordinal, and ratio scales, but rarely is an interval scale employed. The only way to determine what scale is employed in a study is to examine the raw data and note how they were recorded. A key or codebook often will provide this information directly, but it can be determined by inspection. If the record consists only of named units it is nominal, if there is added information that relates to order it is ordinal, if the time that the behavior is recorded is noted it can be considered as interval, and finally, if both time and duration are recorded the scale is ratio.

All scales are subject to issues of accuracy and precision. Accuracy is a statement about how closely the variable measures the issue related to the hypothesis. To employ a sporting analogy, it is an Olympic marksman being able to hit the center of the target. Precision is a statement about how consistent the observer is with the recording of the behavior categories. In the sporting analogy, it is the marksman being able to consistently hit the center of the target (Figure 2.5). The concepts represented here are that bias may shift the behavior record off the target; usually, biases can be accounted for and corrected during an analysis. The failure of precision, which is when the form of the behavior record is variable, can lead to unrecoverable errors and distortion of the data set. Observers need to strive to be both accurate and precise.

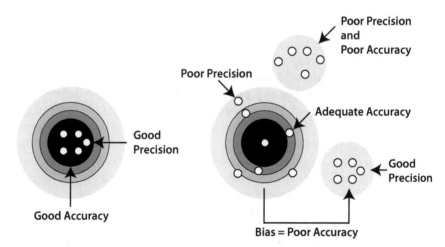

**Figure 2.5** The relationship between accuracy and precision (modified from Lehner 1979:128). The left image shows a good centering on the target (accurate) and a small grouping (high precision). The right image shows the possible combinations of errors. A bias (error of slight adjustment) can lead to a case of poor accuracy but retain good precision. The sights may be set correctly but the operator cannot achieve consistency, leading to adequate accuracy but poor level of precision. Finally both types of errors may be present, as in the upper right grouping which is both off the target (poor accuracy) and widely dispersed (poor precision).

As an example of research design, consider the phenomenon of male dominance hierarchies—the "pecking order" seen among terrestrial Old World monkeys such as the baboons (*Papio* spp.). It is obvious after a short period of observation that a hierarchy ranking males against one another exists but what factors can be used to measure male dominance? Many factors are candidates—fighting skill, body size, ability to make favorable alliances, the favoritism of the group's females, intelligence, or lineage relationships (whom one is related to within the group, and what status they occupy). What behaviors give clues about these factors? To select just one—favoritism of the females, for example—can we see in the behavioral pattern any data leading to the conclusion that "a male has to be a favorite with the females to achieve high rank"? The null hypothesis would be: a male does not have to be a favored partner of the females to achieve high rank.

One factor that might provide data to evaluate these hypotheses is the amount of grooming a male receives and from whom it is received. It becomes possible to construct a study where one focuses on the males in a group and records the amount of grooming received from females, and which females the male grooms in turn. One can then test the hypothesis that the male who receives the most grooming, measured by the number of females participating in grooming him, and/or by the total time of grooming, should be the male who is the most dominant in the male hierarchy. Once the study is done and the statistics calculated, the male with the highest amount of grooming or the largest number of females grooming him should be the most dominant in the hierarchy. If this is the case, the hypothesis fails to be rejected, hence it can be provisionally accepted, but if a different male is most dominant, then the hypothesis is rejected and the null is provisionally accepted. Note that the behavior described in this example may or may not be determinative of male dominance rank, it will depend on the species and/or population you are studying (i.e., it may not be an accurate or valid measure of dominance for a particular species).

The data leading to acceptance or rejection of the hypothesis are representative of only a single variable, and a better design is to utilize different measures related to different factors to reach a valid conclusion. Once the problem is set, the hypotheses formed, and the research design established, the actual conduct of the study and the analysis of the data may turn out to be anticlimactic. In fact, many studies come close to being confirmations of intuitive perceptions formed by the observer before any planning is undertaken. In one sense, this is a perfect model of the scientific method.

A preliminary consideration that saves a great deal of pain and irritation later is some attention to the subsequent data analyses. That is, in the preparation of a research design, it is appropriate and necessary to consider the types of data summarizations and statistical tests that will be used later, and adjust the design and data collection protocols to conform to the analysis requirements. This may merely involve including appropriate spaces on manual check-sheets for summing data, but can be more efficiently calculated when data are uploaded into a software program, such as Excel or Access (Microsoft Corporation). As noted earlier, it is good practice to perform some preliminary analyses after an initial round of data collection; check to see if the data are applicable to the problem, and revise the research plan, data collection protocol, and/or hypotheses as necessary.

# Drawing Conclusions

Students are often intensely concerned with finding some form of "absolute truth" in scientific endeavors, and sadly they must be advised that this objective is impossible. All that science can provide is progressively more accurate representations of what is out there in the real world. In any scientific report stemming from any scientific observation, it is important to recognize what conclusions are possible from the data collected, and what are not. To be exact and precise, one can restrict the report to a straightforward listing of the hypotheses accepted and those rejected, but it is the norm that a degree of interpretation of the results is allowed. However, it is necessary to consider how far this interpretation may go.

While it may be possible to conclude that "a male has to be a favorite with the females to achieve high rank," the causality of the relationship is not defined in the test of the hypothesis. That is, what has been found is a correlation between male rank and male acceptance by the females, there is no causality involved. Explicitly, we cannot say that males have high rank *because* they are favored by the females, nor can we say that males are favored by the females *because* they have a high rank. Other hypotheses and testing are needed to provide such insight into the relationship. Conclusions must be drawn from the data collected and analyzed. If they are not, either it is a failure to recognize what has been found, or it goes beyond the realm of science into the world of speculation.

# Observation Schedules

Many of the exercises in this volume require the use of some form of an observation schedule. The plan for the actual conduct of research work is normally prepared in advance and must enable the worker to complete the study efficiently and in conformity with the requirements of the research design and of the analysis procedures to be used. An observation schedule is like a bus schedule, it is laid out in advance and designed to get to all the stops on the route at fixed times. However, like bus schedules, they tend to get out of control, either running late or missing planned stops.

There are two main kinds of observation schedules, the fixed format and the random sampling schedule. There are also two common variants of random sampling—haphazard and opportunistic (see Lehner 1996:144–147 for discussions of these). The two types of observation schedules both have their useful aspects. The fixed format schedule is best for small groups, short-duration studies, or for the specific experimental sampling of a particular set of members from a larger group. Random sampling is always preferred when the data will be analyzed using inferential statistics. Many researchers, in their attempt to sample randomly, actually sample animals in a haphazard way, such as arbitrarily sampling animals based on convenience (i.e., selecting the animal closest to you or the one that is most active). However, haphazard sampling should be avoided as much as possible as it can bias the data (Lehner 1996). Opportunistic sampling occurs when the researcher chooses to record data at the time the behavior of interest occurs. This can be beneficial for studying rare behaviors but it is not ideal and caution has to be exercised when using statistical approaches on these kinds of data.

## Fixed Format Schedules

Fixed format scheduling is a deliberate process. The observer sets up a working program to collect data from individual subjects at specific times for specific durations. The planning of such a schedule must take into allowance such factors as the climatic conditions, the availability of the subjects, and the requirements of the research design. As an example, during the summer of 1982, Jim Paterson studied the postural and orientation behavior of a set of 10 adult male Japanese macaques (*Macaca fuscata*) at the South Texas Primate Observatory near Dilley, Texas. The research design required a full-day sample for each male, the research period was limited to 32 days, and the daytime maximum temperatures during the period were expected to peak in the 40–45 degree Celsius range. Thus, the use of a fixed format schedule allowing for the collection of 4 or 5 hours of data each day was utilized, and a schedule plotted out for the period specifying which subject was to be the focus of attention for each work-hour (e.g., "if this is Tuesday, July 17th at 1100 hours the focal subject is male #134").

Such rigorous schedules must make allowances for rest periods (for the observer), seek times (the time it takes to find the subject assigned to that sample period), and the possibilities of the climatic conditions or the location of the subject making observation impossible (e.g., rainy days during the wet season). Fixed format scheduling is also the easiest to use for the conduct of studies at a zoological facility. In the wild, finding a certain study subject at a certain time in a location where it is observable can be much more difficult. If the next subject in the rotation cannot be located, it is acceptable to move the next individual in the rotation, and if the study is of sufficient duration (see below), all individuals should receive more or less equal sampling times.

## Random Sampling Schedules

Random sampling schedules are necessary under two circumstances:

1. when the study group is large (and all individual members are being studied over an extended time period), and

2. when the data set is to be analyzed by inferential statistics.

To conduct random sampling, the observer must utilize a procedure that will acceptably produce a random allocation of times to observe particular animals, or of particular animals to observe at specific times. One of the most commonly utilized methods is also the simplest—drawing names or times out of a hat. This process can be conducted in two distinctly different but equally effective ways:

1. The observer creates a set of slips of paper or chips with individual animal identifications on them and then at the beginning of each new sample, merely draws one slip. This slip identifies the next subject to be studied and is then returned to the drawing box or hat. This last act is a vital requirement to guarantee that each subject has the same chance of being drawn for the next sample period.

2. The observer sits down the evening before the workday and does all the drawings for sample periods at one time, returning drawn slips to the box after noting the subjects' identity. The result is a listing of the order of observation for the subjects of the next day. One extra requirement of this process is that a list longer than the intended set of observations be constructed so that if a particular subject cannot be located within a reasonable time, the observer can go onto the next sample, adding the first of the reserve list to the end of the day's sample series.

An alternative—less effective—method is to create a listing of the subjects to be studied, and to then perform the drawing process with slips containing times for the observation sample. This alternative is generally less desirable since it results in a decreasing pool from which to draw, violating a true random distribution. For this reason, we would not suggest this option.

A common alternative procedure for either of the preferred processes listed above is to substitute a set of dice for drawing slips. This does, however, require that each subject be allocated a number and that each number is capable of being generated by a random throw of the dice. Those who are familiar with fantasy role-playing games might consider the use of more complex dice than the traditional cubic form and may be able to find dice with appropriate numbers of sides for most occasions and group sizes. However, a more appropriate procedure is to employ a stratified partition method such as that detailed in exercise 3. One can also use mobile apps (e.g., "Research Randomizer") to determine the random sampling schedules.

The apparent inequities of the random sampling process, and the inevitable cases where the same subject is selected for several consecutive sampling sessions, may lead one to conclude that the selection process is biased; however, all the factors balance out if the study is of sufficient length. Thus, a secondary requirement is that the study must be long enough in duration that the random selection process can have the opportunity to bring the sample sizes for all the subjects up to approximately the same level, over the same study hours. This allows the research process to reach a truly random sampling of the behaviors of the group. However, for most short-term projects, and the exercises in this book, a fixed observing schedule can be more effective.

## Setting Up Check-Sheets

While there are different ways to record data, the oldest and most commonly utilized is some form of the check-sheet. A check-sheet may range from a simple blank page to a highly structured instrument geared toward precise and complex observation. As Hinde (1973:393) has said, "While the design of a check-sheet seems a simple matter, experience shows that there are snags that may handicap research efforts." Every researcher and every project are different, and thus "every check-sheet must be designed with an eye to the problem in hand and to the idiosyncrasies of the observer" (Hinde 1973:393). Because of these features, there can be no "standard" check-sheet, however, there are principles that can be employed to guide the design of a functional sheet related to a research question.

A check-sheet always requires two main components:

1. *Data Management and Control Areas*. These are normally placed at the top of the sheet, and provide the information about the observer, the date and times of observation, special control factors, and other items that may be relevant to the analysis.

2. *The Data Collection Fields*. These cover the remainder of the check-sheet and should be constructed in a form related to the sampling protocol and the recording method.

A simple check-sheet may be constructed with only a limited amount of control data and a minimum of categories, as in this example in Figure 2.6. The control data consist only of the observer identity and the date and times of start and stop. Because the sheet was designed to deal with a simple categorization of primate mating behaviors, there are only three columns and the record consists solely of a tally count of these as perceived by the observer. Clearly, this simple sheet provides a limited amount of control information and data. It has limited utility and can only provide a frequency count of "presents," "mounts," and "copulations" by an unknown number of individuals during the observational time. The most useful data coming from such a record would be a rate of occurrence.

Hinde (1973) presented an example of a significantly more complex check-sheet where there is a column for time, another for the identity of the subject

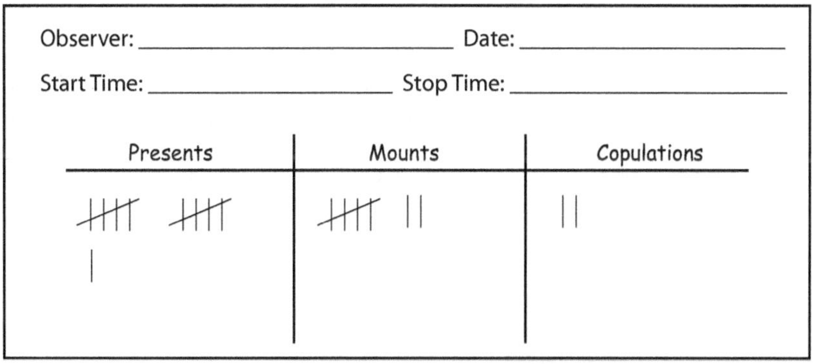

**Figure 2.6** A simple check-sheet. Modified from Bakeman and Gottman 1997:41.

chimpanzee, and five sets of columns for tallies or notes on behaviors that might occur, plus a larger column for "comments." This is typical for an actual operational check-sheet (Figure 2.7).

Time control is often a requirement of modern research designs, either as regular intervals or as a continuous record. While examples of appropriate check-sheets for these will be found in the appropriate exercises, it may be worthwhile remembering an older approach sometimes called "lined paper recording." This is a manually operated version of the data-recording style generated by electronic devices. The structure of such a check-sheet is straightforward. The first column is for time, at appropriate intervals, and the remaining columns are coded for particular behaviors. Thus, the sheet has columns of behaviors horizontally and time in intervals arrayed vertically. The observer may use checkmarks or simply draw a line in the appropriate column from the start of the behavior to its end. Such a check-sheet would look like Figure 2.8.

Interpretation of the data in such a sheet is simple. Behavior "A" occurred from time 1 to 4, and time 11 to 13, in both cases associated with "Sit" posture, but also with "Lay" from time 3 to 4. This layout could be employed for both continuous-time recording, through leaving the time column blank and writing times of behavior or posture changes, or for interval time recording with regular times printed in. It is, however, limited to a preconceptualized and predefined set of behaviors and/or variables. Data falling outside of these parameters can only be added under the informal "remarks" area. Every observer will eventually need to design and test check-sheets for particular observational problems, and students can use the exercises in this book to practice this activity. However, for many of the exercises, sample check-sheets are provided to spend time observing rather than constructing check-sheets.

| TIME | CHIMP | arrival | CALL | FACE | charge | hair out | bipedal | slap | stampcharge | drag | branch wave | throw (object) | drum | CHASE | CONTACT I | CONTACT II | ARM THREAT | APPROACH | GROOM | BY | HUNCH | EMBRACE | KISS | EXTEND HAND | TOUCH | SEX | BOB | CROUCH | PRESENT | CLOSE FACE | AVOID | NO RESPONSE | BOTTOM CONDITION | COMMENTS |
|---|---|---|---|---|---|---|---|---|---|---|---|---|---|---|---|---|---|---|---|---|---|---|---|---|---|---|---|---|---|---|---|---|---|---|
| 1200 | HM | ✓ | Ph | | ✓ | ✓ | | 1 | | | | 2 | 3 | | | | | | | | | | | | | | | | | | | | | Throws rock |
| 1230 | FG | ✓ | Ph | | ✓ | ✓ | | 2 | | 3 | 1 | | | | | | | | | | | | | | | | | | | | | | | Drags branch |
| | SW | | Sc | | | | | | | | | | | | | | | | SW SW | SW | | | | | | | | | | | | | | |
| 1238 | FG | | | | | ✓ | | | | | | | | | | | | SW | FG | FG | | | | | | | | | FG | | FG | | | up tree |
| | SW | | Pg | | | | | | | | | | | SW | | | | | | | | | | | | | | | | | | | | |
| 1300 | MK | | | | ✓ | ✓ | | | | | | | | SW | | | | | | | SW | | | | | SW | | | | | | | | See sex |
| | SW | | Pb | | ✓ | | | | | | | | | | | | | M3K | | | | | | | | M3K | | | M3K | | M3K | | | up tree then approach |

**Figure 2.7** Check-sheet for recording particular types of behavior when they occurred in chimpanzees arriving at the Gombe Stream Research Center (Hinde 1973:402 based on personal communication from Halperin).

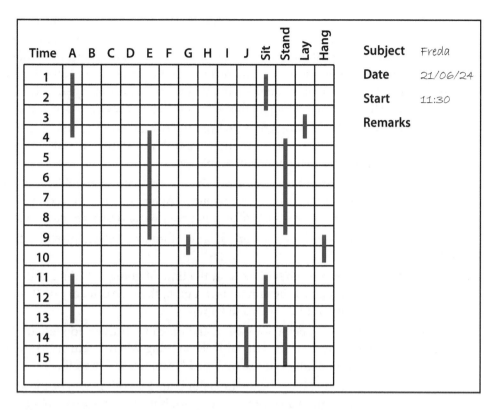

**Figure 2.8**   Lined paper record check-sheet for 10 behaviors and four postures.

## The "Out-of-Sight" Problem

In any observational study, whether it is conducted in the wild or at an enclosure in a zoological park, one of the consistent problems that surfaces is what to do when a subject moves into an unobservable area, or part of the enclosure. While it is impossible to plan around this when observing in the wild, there are variable policies in zoological parks. Sometimes animals are locked out of portions of their habitat for substantial periods, while in other cases, the subjects may have complete access to all areas—on and off display—throughout the day. It is generally appropriate to inquire as to the policies with the zookeepers and to modify research designs to accommodate these variations.

Where it is possible for a subject to escape from the observer's view, it is necessary for the observer to include a category of behavior simply labeled as "out-of-sight." This naturally leads to another situation requiring a policy decision within the research design: At what point does one terminate and discard a sample due to an extended out-of-sight condition? This is an arbitrary decision on the part of the observer, but it makes little sense to include samples in a study where the animal is out-of-sight for more than half of the sample.

There are six mechanisms to deal with the problems arising from the out-of-sight condition. Four of these are discussed by Lehner (1996:193), but as he clearly notes "none of these methods [are] truly valid," and statisticians often cringe at the suggestion of using one or more of the techniques. Note that all introduce some form of bias into the data. Where the out-of-sight period is long in relation to the normal duration of the behaviors, Lehner suggests two variants:

1. Deletion of the out-of-sight time from the overall sample. The length of the sample, in this case, is reduced, and many statistical tests are not able to handle data in noncomparable blocks.

2. Time-out. Suspend observation for the period that the animal is out-of-sight, resuming the sample on its return. Again, this is a procedure that can bias the results of statistical tests in unknown and unforeseeable ways.

When the out-of-sight periods are of short duration, Lehner provides two alternates:

1. Allocate the same behavior seen at the time of going out-of-sight to the whole period (e.g., if the animal is foraging, then the category of "foraging" continues until it returns to view).

2. Allocate the same behavior seen at the time of returning to view to the whole period (e.g., if the animal is locomoting when it returns to sight, then the out-of-sight period is assigned "locomoting" as well).

Lehner suggests that if the behavior is the same for both methods, the allocation of the out-of-sight behavior is more valid; however, this may not necessarily follow. Lehner only provides a relative guideline, and no fixed rule is readily available.

The two other solutions are more direct but also have statistical or research consequences. One solution is to utilize the category of out-of-sight as a regular behavioral unit and employ it within the statistical analysis. This may have the simple advantage of not biasing the statistical procedures, but it clearly intrudes a substantial element of uncertainty into the data. Treating out-of-sight in this fashion can have untoward research effects that may be variable across the diurnal cycle for instance. This yields a distortion of the data despite being in statistical compliance.

The final option is to establish a protocol rule dealing with how much out-of-sight time can be tolerated. One suggestion is that an absolute limit to out-of-sight time totals no more than one-third of the sample time as the point at which the sample should be discarded. That is, if the out-of-sight time exceeds 5 minutes in a 15-minute sample, the sample is discarded and another sample started. Or, the out-of-sight time could total no more than 10% of the total sample time, which is commonly employed in many primatology studies.

However, it might be decided that out-of-sight conditions are not representative of the behavior of the subject animal and the tolerance for this category may be set at zero, hence discarding a sample as soon as the subject leaves the area of view. The downside is that this results in a larger number of discarded samples and the collection of a limited number of valid samplings during each working session. These are decisions that each observer must make, but the pattern must be consistent throughout the data collection phase. Observers may feel guilty about throwing away samples in this fashion, but it is important to realize that it could be far worse to include all the out-of-sight records and wind up biasing the analysis. Each observer will see the occurrence and effects of out-of-sight records in different ways and consequently, each researcher's protocols and research design will be different. It is important to include a protocol—some combination of the ways to deal with the out-of-sight problem—in the research design and know what to do when the situation inevitably arises.

## Selection of a Subject Species and Captive vs. Free-Ranging/Wild

One last issue in research design must be dealt with before proceeding, and that is the issue of "choosing" a subject species. This may be perceived as irrelevant by those individuals who are "locked in" on a specific species as their focus of interest. They are restricted in their selection of research questions to those that can be conducted with their favored species.

There are five basic considerations in the selection of a species for a particular research question, and these have been succinctly gathered together by Lehner (1996):

- *Suitability.* The August Krogh Principle asks, "Is the species suitable for the concept being studied?" One first defines the research problem, searches for a species that displays the relevant behavior, and investigates whether it exhibits the behavior frequently enough to provide adequate data. It must also be possible to observe the species and the behavior of interest for it will do no good to the project if the activity is largely conducted out-of-sight.

- *Availability.* Can you easily go to the subjects or have the subjects brought to you? Two primary conditions exist. The first: If the species is not locally available and must be studied in the field, what are the political issues? Is it possible to conduct research in the country or countries where the animals exist? What restrictions or permits have to be obtained, how are they administered, are fees payable for the permits, can the permits be obtained before arrival in the country? Any and all potential problems with the legal and political establishments must be considered.

  The second: Is the species accessible? Can they be easily observed? Is the species nocturnal, diurnal, or crepuscular? Do your personal habits fit with the animal's schedules? If certain biological samples are important to your project, can these be accessed? For example, fecal samples are relatively easily obtained in the field and much information can be gleaned from their analyses but certain types of data may require the collection of urine or saliva. How feasible is it to get these types of materials from your study subjects (see chapter 5 for more information on this)? If your project requires observation of laboratory animals, or if you are considering studying captive animals, then different problems arise, along with a host of ethical considerations for laboratory animals, particularly. The following general questions should be addressed; however, it is recommended to consult McCann et al. (2007) for further information in the study of laboratory primates, and Rees (2015) for captive animals.

- *Adaptability.* Has the animal adapted to captivity? Are there any special caretaking needs that may interfere with the experimental protocols (for captive projects)? Are your lifestyle patterns compatible with your subjects?

- *Available Data.* What is already known about the species? Perhaps your research question has already been tested. Is there a good background data set? If there is, will these data help to answer the foregoing questions and anticipate problems?

- *Decision Time.* The positives and negatives related to these criteria must be added up and an evaluation of the financial commitment involved factored in before choosing to accept or reject the species as the subject for your investigation.

# THREE

# Defining, Describing, and Coding Behavior

# What Is Behavior?

The term "behavior" is widely defined in literature. Definitions run from a simplistic "behavior is what an animal does," to Hinde's (1973:393) statement, "behavior consists of a complex nexus of events in time," and even to Heraclitus of Ephesus' famous philosophical dictum "you can never step into the same river twice." What all such statements are attempting to do is provide some empirical, rational mechanism for describing and categorizing the acts, actions, and interactions of our subjects. Therefore, behavior can be defined as a specific response to a stimulus, or as a repertoire of responses to stimuli (Rees 2015).

Input comes in the form of external and internal stimuli, is processed within the animal's nervous system (often referred to as a "black box" where we do not fully understand all the processes involved), and the visible response is the behavior in question. In most behavioral research, the underlying neural mechanisms of the behavior do not need to be fully understood to study the causes and consequences of the behavior itself; however, certain physiological or psychological studies may focus on the underlying processes involved.

# Behavior and Perception

It is important for the beginning researcher to recognize and remember that a behavior record of the activities of subject animals is a mental construct of the observer, and as such is subject to bias and distortion that may divorce the reality of the subject's action from the perceived and recorded observations. For an observer to record behavior that is "seen," a moderately complex neural pathway is traversed by the information. The image is then compared and contrasted, and recognition, pattern-seeking functions are employed to interpret what the image is and associate it with a meaning. The most dramatic insertion of biases and selective perceptions take place at this level.

People may only see what they want to see, even when they are trying to be objective. For example, while one might describe a human smile as "progressive stretching of the orbis oralis muscle toward the auricles by the levator oralis muscles, accompanied by a slight parting of contact between the surfaces of the lips," we tend to perceive the action as simply a "smile," and, in an anthropomorphic interpretation (i.e., one specific to our species), to impute various "friendly" emotions to the action. In many other species, this action pattern would be considered threatening, appearing as an "intention to bite" or a variant of "tense mouth face" (described later as a low-level threat signal).

To partially correct this set of problems, it is important to aid in the control of one's perceptual biases by developing specific descriptions of all behaviors that will be incorporated into a study as part of the study design. For illustration, see van Hoof's (1967) catalog of primate facial configurations (Figure 3.1).

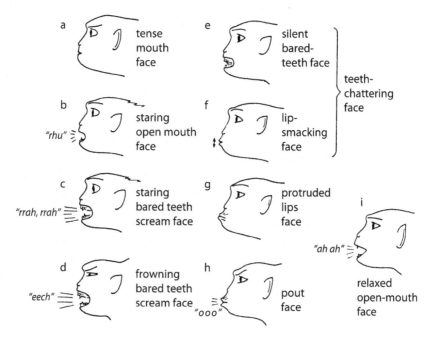

**Figure 3.1**  Schematic facial expressions and names for some *Macaca* spp. (van Hooff 1967:64).

## Describing Behavior

As Hinde (1973:393) says: "Before [behavior] can be studied it must be described, broken down into units suitable for study, and the units classified into groups according to common properties." This statement clearly implies that there is a difference between *behavior* and *behavior records*. The former is truly the stream of operation of the organism, the latter is the record produced by the observer. To some extent this may seem like a restatement of the philosophical conundrum "If a tree falls in the forest and there is no one to hear, does it make a sound?" but it is not. What it implies is that the organism is independent of the observer, it performs (sometimes it is said to "exhibit") a stream of behavior, not all of which is visible or audible, and the record produced by the observer has been filtered through the neural system of a different organism. The record is therefore an abstract of what the observer saw, which in turn is an abstract of what the organism did.

Often it is assumed that the definition of behavior is determined at or near the beginning of a study. Unfortunately, defining behavior requires a degree of experience with the subject species and their activities (known as a "repertoire of behaviors") that the observer does not have at the beginning of the study. In addition, not all behaviors are observed during the initial phases of a study so new behavior definitions will need to be added, but at progressively less frequent intervals until the project ends. In ordinary terms, it may be possible to record a large portion of an organism's behavior repertoire in ten to a hundred hours, and it may be possible to record 99% of that repertoire in 10,000 hours, but it is unlikely that the book can ever be closed on the behavioral catalog.

Before embarking on the development of formal definitions, the normal process requires some thought and attention to the classification of behavior. An initial visit around the zoological gardens and a few minutes of *ad hoc* observing often suggests that this process is relatively simple and easily accomplished. However, as Altmann (1968) noted, categorizing the units of social behavior involves one major decision: when to split and when to lump. The boundaries between behaviors developed by the observer are meant to reflect the splitting and lumping that the subjects themselves do rather than arbitrary acts of the observer. The complex behavioral units separate out behaviors that occur simultaneously either within one organism or coordinated between several individuals. Walking and talking (in humans), hanging and feeding, resting and being in social proximity would be examples.

Lehner (1996) identifies two types of behavior description: *empirical* and *functional*. Empirical descriptions describe the behavior in terms of body parts, movements and postures (e.g., baring the teeth). Functional descriptions refer to the behavior's function, proximally or ultimately (e.g., bared-teeth threat). The type of behavior description employed will depend on the observer's knowledge of the species' repertoire as well as the research questions imposed by the study. According to Lehner (1996), functional descriptions can be highly interpretive and involve anthropomorphism, where humans project human behavior onto nonhuman animals (e.g., using terms such as "love" or "jealousy"). As unbiased, objective observers of primate behavior, we should avoid anthropomorphism where possible. To avoid using misleading terms, Lehner (1996) suggests using more empirical versus functional descriptions of behavior, and using more technical definitions can help to clarify behavior descriptions.

## Formal Definitions of Behavior

An ethogram is a list of behaviors that represent the behavioral repertoire of a species (Lehner 1996). Ethograms can vary in breadth and depth, depending on the study and research questions employed. In an ethogram (see exercise 2) formal definitions of behaviors are required, but the amount of detail employed in a definition is variable. As a general format for a formal definition, it is suggested that a clear description breaking the behavior into as many level descriptors as is appropriate be generated. It is also a cardinal rule of philology that the definition may not include the term being defined. That means a definition of "sleeping" as "being asleep" or "the activity of sleeping" is not acceptable. For example, the following is a good functional definition of "sleeping": remaining in a relaxed posture with closed eyes, regular breathing, and apparent unconsciousness. However, it must be acknowledged that there may be variations around this definition. For instance, some humans are able to sleep with their eyes either half or fully open (the key then becomes the absence of the blinking normally seen in conscious individuals). So a more complete definition for sleeping may be: remaining in a relaxed posture, usually with closed eyes, regular breathing, a lack of blinking, and apparent unconciousness.

A second requirement for a formal definition is that it be mutually exclusive and extensive. This means that the overlap between behavior categories is undesirable, and the behavioral repertoire should fill all the observation time. An observer developing a list of defined behaviors needs to take care that there is no overlap between them. This can be challenging to tease apart, but necessary. Understanding the following elements can help in this process.

## Hierarchy of Behavioral Units

Behavior units can often be grouped together and arranged in a hierarchy, and confusion over the level in a hierarchy where a behavior belongs can establish an apparent overlap condition. As a simple example, the observer may note that "grooming" behavior is a favored activity in most primate species, but that the activity of picking through hair and over skin, extracting debris and parasites, occurs in three possible modes. These are self- or "autogrooming," where the action is directed toward the subject's body areas; "giving groom," one form of "allogrooming" in which the subject actively grooms a different individual; and "receive groom," the other form of allogrooming in which the subject receives the grooming attention of another individual. Thus, a hierarchy of grooming exists with first level subdivisions of auto- and allogrooming, and a second level under allogroom separating giving and receiving grooming.

## Individual vs. Social, Static vs. Dynamic

A classic problem beginning observers have in classification is distinguishing *individual* from *social* behaviors, and further delineating *static* from *dynamic* behaviors (Delgado and Delgado 1962). Individual behaviors involve "the system in relation to itself, or its environment" (e.g., a primate feeding), whereas social behaviors involve the "interrelation of the systems of the same class" (e.g., a primate food-sharing) (Delgado and Delgado 1962:260–261). Static behaviors can be identified as those that are fixed in relation to the systems (e.g., a primate sleeping), whereas dynamic behaviors involve a sequence of spatial relations (e.g., a primate running). With the injunction to record a behavior for all the time involved, students often feel obliged to record whether the subject is sitting, lying, hanging, prone, or supine. These then become translated into "behavioral categories" and included within the ethogram.

While the distinction provided by Delgado and Delgado between *static* and *dynamic* seems to suggest this is appropriate, an observer must note that these categories are not on different arms of the hierarchy (i.e., they are all "resting"), and hence they should be merged. The reason behind this is that static and dynamic categories imply variables that are different yet can be recorded simultaneously, and they may not correlate with each other. It is entirely possible to record an animal in a particular posture (e.g., sitting) and note that, for some of the time, it is "resting," for some it is "scanning," and for some it is "receiving grooming." The situation is one where there may be one posture but there are three distinct behaviors being performed. Similarly, while receiving grooming, a subject may be seen as "sitting," "lying supine," "lying prone," and "standing quadrupedally." There is sufficient justification for the separation of static and dynamic behavior. However, it should also be noted that the action of assuming a posture, such as "sitting up" or "sitting down" is appropriate dynamic behavior and should be recorded as such.

## Fixed and Variable Behavior Patterns

While most of the twentieth century saw a great deal of argument about the causal origin of behavior, the currently accepted paradigm is that most behavior units have roots in *nature* and *nurture*. This is largely a consequence of the fusion between European classical ethology and American comparative psychology, which occurred at the end of the 1960s and led to the defining of behavioral ecology. Despite this, there are behaviors that can be categorized as being strongly biologically determined; i.e., they belong more on the nature side of the issue.

There are two degrees of these natural behaviors, the ones that are ritualized and those that constitute displays. Behavior is said to be ritualized in an organism when it presents three characteristics: (1) it is stereotypical within the species (it is of the same form and pattern throughout the studied representatives of the species); (2) it can be shown to have been shaped by natural selection; and (3) it can be shown to be strongly controlled by genetic mechanisms. It can be a substantial problem to verify this attribution of ritualized behavior without an extensive and complex research endeavor; consequently, most of the claims of ritualization are founded on logical arguments and patterns of stereotypy.

The extreme form of ritualization is display behavior. A display is a ritualized signal that is exaggerated, more stereotypic, and incorporates several elements that make it complex in form. Almost any behavioral element can be incorporated into a display. A display may include autonomic responses of the sympathetic and parasympathetic nervous systems, such as piloerection (erection of the hair over some area or the entire body), vascular changes (such as color changes in the face, hands, or sexual skin areas due to increased blood flow), intention movements, displacement movements, and other signals. An example of a sequence of display behaviors occurs in the aggressive behavior of most cercopithecoids. The sequence of *headbob*—a brief dropping and raising of the head, *forebob*—a brief dropping of the whole front of the body, looking like a half pushup, *bounce*—where the aggressive animal jumps a half step forward, landing on all four limbs at the same time, then jumps back, and *branch shake*—in which either a vertical or a horizontal structure is forcefully slammed by the hind feet while holding on with the forelimbs, often causing the support to sway dramatically, represent increasing intensity of aggressive signaling. However, perhaps one of the most common displays (in the cercopithecoids, at least) is the *eyelid flash*, an aggressive signal in which the eyes are blinked or the eyebrows are raised to show the contrasting colored eyelid patches as shown in Figure 3.2. With these concepts in hand, a student of behavior can proceed to the development of a listing of observed behaviors and can set up appropriate nonredundant, mutually exclusive definitions of the categories.

**Figure 3.2** Threatening lid display of an adult male gelada (*Theropithecus gelada*). Oleg Senkov/Shutterstock.

# Coding Behavior for Data Recording

As might be evident by this point, a simple list of behaviors is not the only item necessary for the conduct of scientific observation. Also required is a grammar for the record construction. There are only a few possible grammars that fill the needs of the observer. The grammar must be simple to learn, straightforward to record, and it must adequately represent the stream of behavior of the subject. The most appropriate for general use is one that parallels the "Subject–Verb–Predicate" structure of most Western languages, in the form of "Actor–Act–Recipient."

The "Actor–Act–Recipient" grammar is suited to all the sampling procedures recommended by Altmann (1974) and is amenable to utilization in analysis and statistical testing. Because the "actor" in this grammar may or may not be the focal subject, it is necessary to develop a second set of categories to allow for the focal to passively receive acts from an actor that is not the focal. Since in focal sampling the intent is to record everything that the focal does as actor, the observer must also be equipped to record everything that happens to the focal as "recipient."

Our sample record from chapter 2 reflects this grammar in the structure of the sample:

```
 1  10:32:22   Jo-Jo receives grooming from Jay-Jay
 2  10:34:36   Jo-Jo sits up
 3  10:34:37   Jo-Jo locomotes to food dish
 4  10:34:41   Jo-Jo eating
 5  10:36:12   Jo-Jo drinks
 6  10:36:12   Jo-Jo scratches
 7  10:36:13   Jo-Jo chases Spike
 8  10:36:55   Jo-Jo receives threat from Alice
 9  10:36:56   Jo-Jo presents to Alice
10  10:36:57   Jo-Jo receives grooming from Alice
```
*(line numbers added for referencing)*

A moment of inspection will result in noting that record lines 2, 3, 4, 5, 6, 7, and 9 are in the active mode—Jo-Jo is *doing* something—while record lines 1, 8, and 10 are in the passive mode—Jo-Jo is *having something done* to him. Naturally, if this was a focal animal sample record, then Jo-Jo's name would not be present on every record line but would be in the heading information and a check-sheet with this record would look like something like the following:

Focal Subject: Jo-Jo
Sample Duration: 10 minutes
Weather: Bright Sun, No wind, Temperature 21°C.
Location: Quadrat B12, small clearing.

| | |
|---|---|
| 10:32:22 | receives grooming from Jay-Jay |
| 10:34:36 | sits up |
| 10:34:37 | locomotes to food dish |
| 10:34:41 | eating |
| 10:36:12 | drinks |
| 10:36:12 | scratches |
| 10:36:13 | chases Spike |
| 10:36:55 | receives threat from Alice |
| 10:36:56 | presents to Alice |
| 10:36:57 | receives grooming from Alice. |

Now that grammar has been specified (alternative grammars will not be considered in this workbook) with some idea of how it contributes to the study of animal behavior, it is appropriate to turn to the practicalities. Writing the data down in longhand, or even typing it out can be tedious and prone to error, so a common feature of most recording protocols is a code. Codes can vary greatly between individual observers, just as the decisions about the boundaries between behaviors vary. In general, a code that consists of one or two or three letters, a mnemonic, based on the behavior label or name is satisfactory. Thus, one can set up a codebook where the behavior label or name is listed along with the code to be used and the definition of the behavior itself. A two or three letter code may have the following "rg" or "rgm" for "receive groom from," "st" for "sits up," "fd" for "feeding/eating," "dr" or "drk" for "drinking," "scr" for "scratching," "ggm" for "giving grooming," and "pr" for "present to," and would result in the previous check-sheet being transformed into a more compact record.

Focal Subject: Jo-Jo
Sample Duration: 10 minutes
Weather: Bright Sun, No wind, Temperature 21°C.
Location: Quadrat B12, small clearing.

| | |
|---|---|
| 10:32:22 | rg Jay-Jay |
| 10:34:36 | st |
| 10:34:37 | loc dish |
| 10:34:41 | fd |
| 10:36:12 | dr |
| 10:36:12 | scr |
| 10:36:13 | ch Spike |
| 10:36:55 | ragr Alice |
| 10:36:56 | pr Alice |
| 10:36:57 | rg Alice. |

The key feature of the coding scheme is the application of the KISS principle. KISS is a well-worn acronym for "Keep It Simple, Stupid," and along with the well-known GIGO rule (Garbage In, Garbage Out) should be applied to the development of a code. Overly complex or unusual mnemonics can make the code confusing to the operator and lead to errors of commission through recording an inappropriate code unit. This can be especially important where the observer is not the originator of the code or when there are multiple observers for the same research project.

The only remaining problem for the observer is accurate time control, and how precisely the time must be recorded. While various timing algorithms have been published for use in computer-based data collection programs emphasizing intervals accurate to 1/10th, 1/100th, and even 1/1000th of a second, such precision for field data is not usually necessary. It is important to understand that there is a "reaction time loop"—the period in which the observer sees the change of behavior, recognizes what the newly initiated behavior is, decides on the appropriate code, and performs the physical actions necessary to make the record, whether writing two to ten characters or hitting them on a keyboard. A good rule of thumb is to record to an accuracy of one (1) second, and this applies equally to the pencil and paper recording system.

Under normal conditions, an observer will rarely operate faster than a one half second interval, and to be fair to the subject, will an error of ± 0.5 seconds make a significant difference to the data collected? Indeed, over a longer study period, the randomization of such observer errors will tend toward a net effect of zero. It can be argued that human observers and animal subjects can in fact perform behaviors at faster rates, and that millisecond timing is required. While there may be some merit to the argument, the only truly accurate way to deal with such timing concerns is through the use of video or film and slow speed analysis. Such precision is not possible *in vivo*. It would be unlikely for any observer to seriously attempt millisecond precision timing on any field project; the demands in time and energy and the resultant volume of data are excessive.

## Operationalizing the Observational Study

Utilizing the KISS and GIGO principles in conjunction with the model of the scientific method, we are now ready to begin the operational planning of the study project. We can proceed using the following outline:

- *Do we have a research question?* This is an absolute necessity since we will be attempting to find out something about the world.

- *Do we have a set of hypotheses?* These descend from the research question and must be phrased in a testable fashion (meaning they must be answerable as either yes or no, or in some cases with a predicted direction).

- *Have we chosen a sampling method?* The choice of sampling method depends on whether the research project is behavior- or individual-oriented, and is correlated with the recording rule chosen.

- *Has a recording rule been selected?* Either continuous or interval recording is statistically appropriate, but care must be taken to choose the most relevant method.

- *Are the variables set up?* Are the variables able to measure the relevant behaviors in useful ways? These form the central core of the research project; without them, and without their verification, the entire project is invalid.

- *Have we selected the appropriate statistical procedures for our hypotheses and our variables?* It is always a good strategy to have a clear understanding of the statistical procedures relevant to the data to be collected. In many cases, the choice of a statistic will limit the data and the method of collection.

- *Have we dealt with all the necessary protocol approvals from granting agencies or Animal Care Committees (ACC or IACUC; see chapter 1 for more information)?* Most colleges, universities, and zoological societies must have ACC committees if they are involved in nonhuman animal research. Have we obtained appropriate research/export/import permits from governments? The latter is only relevant when a field expedition is required, but the paperwork is part of the process and IACUC approvals are almost always required.

- *Have we dealt with the logistics of the project?* Health, accommodation, travel documents, customs registrations, financial transfers, or other considerations? If our project takes us into the tropics, as is likely for primatological research, we must devote a substantial amount of time to dealing with these issues.

When all these points have been dealt with, the only things remaining are to do the work: perform the observations, collect the data, analyze them, and write up the results. At that point, and only at that point, is a cycle of the scientific process complete, but assuredly the effort has led to the generation of more new questions than have been answered. Welcome to the world of science!

# Measuring Social Behavior

Almost all primate species (with a few exceptions) are highly social and live in groups with adult female/s, male/s, and offspring. Some groups are small, consisting of a bonded pair and their offspring, others are large, with over 100 animals, and still others can have complex, multilevel societies with hundreds or even up to 1,000 animals. How do individuals within and between groups navigate what can be a complex social milieu? Certainly, having a large brain (compared to most mammals) helps in this regard. But how do large-brained human observers unravel the underlying social relationships among individual primates? Understanding primate sociality can seem a daunting task, but it is critical to advancing our broader knowledge of primate ecology, behavior, and even conservation.

Analyzing, modeling, and interpreting primate societies can involve a level of complexity that goes beyond this volume (see Whitehead 2008 for a complete review of methods and analyses); however, the basic analytical tools used by primatologists are not overly difficult to master and can often be applied to understanding sociality in other social animals. Hinde (1976) provided a basic framework that has been widely incorporated into the analyses of primate societies (Figure 4.1). The framework begins with observing the interactions among individuals, the fundamental element of social behavior (Whitehead 2008). Often, this entails interactions that occur between two particular individuals, or a dyad. Thus, when a dyad is involved in an interaction, the two individuals are known to be in "association" with one another whether it is affiliative, agonistic, or neutral (see below for more information on these types of behaviors).

The types of behaviors (i.e., the content—if the behaviors are more affiliative or agonistic) and the quality and patterning of the interactions observed determine the nature of the social relationship between the individuals. In turn, the nature of those social relationships determines (along with other factors such as ecology, phylogeny, population density, and predation pressure) the overall social structure of a group or species. Note that we use the term "social structure" as defined by Kappeler and van Schaik (2002), but the definition of this term can vary in the literature (e.g., sometimes the term "social organization" is used in the same way).

In any analyses of social behavior, it is important to be able to reliably identify study subjects to the level of the individual (see exercise 1 for further information); however, some basic analyses can be achieved by identifying study subjects to the level of age-sex class.

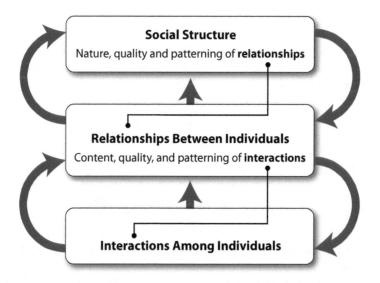

**Figure. 4.1** Hinde's (1976) conceptual framework for analyzing primate societies. Adapted from Whitehead 2008.

# Affiliative and Agonistic Behaviors

Much of primate social behavior can be categorized as either *affiliative* (friendly kinds of behaviors), or *agonistic* (unfriendly or competitive behaviors), with various levels of intensity associated with each. Affiliative behaviors can include social interactions such as grooming, and sitting or resting near other individuals (often referred to as "proximity" or "nearest neighbor" behavior). Under this umbrella term, one can also observe "affinitive" behaviors, or those behaviors where an individual is attracted to or "liking" another individual. Grooming can determine underlying social relationships within dyads, and in many species that groom regularly, grooming interactions are performed either up or down the hierarchy predictably. So, either the groomer (one who performs or directs the grooming) or the groomee (one who receives the grooming) tend to be dominant to the other, depending on the species. Recording regular grooming interactions can help determine the group dominance hierarchy. However, grooming also occurs in egalitarian species (where all individuals tend to have equal access to resources, i.e., no dominance hierarchies); thus, grooming interactions can also help to determine closer, or friendlier social relationships among individuals.

Less directional forms of affiliative behavior include proximity (who is sitting/resting near whom, at what distance, and for how long), which can also help to determine friendly social relationships among individuals. Conversely, agonistic behaviors can range in intensity from highly aggressive interactions such as biting, chasing, or lunging, to less intense forms of aggression including submissive and appeasement behaviors such as one individual avoiding another individual. Agonistic behaviors can be used to determine social and dominance relationships within dyads, and dominance hierarchies within groups.

## Proximity or Nearest-Neighbor Studies

Other questions related to patterns of social interaction among individual primates include: Do some individuals form regular or consistent subgroupings within their group? If so, do these subgroupings change during a daily cycle or with different activities? Are subgroups determined by rank, or are they a consequence of rank seeking? One method of answering these questions that is appropriate and straightforward is a proximity, or "nearest neighbor" study. These data allow you to determine who is associating, when, and how closely.

The basic premise for studies of group structure and underlying social relationships is that individuals can be found in association because they prefer to be with some group members and avoid other individuals.

Numerous research designs can be constructed to employ nearest neighbor data and successfully yield information about the social structure of a primate group. Basic data collected in such a study might be the distance from a focal individual to others, and the duration of time that neighbors are in different distance categories. An error frequently seen in these studies involves assuming that the observer can precisely judge distances between individual subjects from all observation distances. It is inappropriate to use a small scale, such as one that employs one- or half-meter intervals out to 10 or more meters between subjects. The precision is unjustified, and for all but a phenomenal few, unachievable. Such fine-grained differences in distance may also be meaningless in terms of their validity. It is far more useful and practical to use a scale consisting of, for example: in contact; within arm's reach; within three meters; beyond three meters. It is seldom necessary to employ a finer grain, and it is difficult to verify the observer's accuracy at distance judgment.

To best determine the appropriate distances, consult the literature for the species or population in question, and follow similar methods if available. To retain accuracy in judging distances, and to ensure consistency among different observers, you can set up different distances (using measuring tapes or similar) before embarking on your study, and practice judging them from different perspectives and distances. Like reliability tests, you can continue testing all observers until there is an overwhelming agreement (although there is no mathematical way to test this, to our knowledge). It would also be important to continue intermittent testing to ensure consistency throughout a study.

The proximity patterns can be statistically analyzed only when data about identified individuals and their distances from each other are available. Proximity data can also be used to assess the "sociability" of individual animals and the social relationships within dyads. If individuals are constantly in a cluster with close contact, their rating would be higher on the scale of sociability than if they were rarely in any association or kept other individuals at greater distances. Dyads regularly in association indicate preferred relationships (sometimes called "friendships") between those individuals.

## Association Measurements

### Constructing an Interaction Matrix

A first step in analyzing associations involves constructing a matrix of interactions (or sociometric matrix). Matrices are two-axis tables that are organized with the actors along one axis and the recipients along the other (in the case of an asymmetric data set of interactions) and include either raw data totals or rates of interactions. They may also include row and column totals, depending on the data presented. Matrices can be used to present grooming, proximity, or agonistic interaction data, among others; however, each matrix is restricted to one specific behavior pattern. Thus, to begin a matrix analysis it is necessary to have data that records the actor who emits the behavior, and the recipient who is the receiver of the behavior. This means that it is also necessary to have, at minimum, category level identification, and preferably individual recognition to be able to make records in the form: "George (male 321) aggressed against Ralph (male 456), who fled." These are the kinds of data that are collected in focal animal or continuous sampling (exercise 9). If these types of data are available, then it is relatively simple to construct the matrix.

Table 4.1 provides an example of total grooming time among individuals within a hypothetical group of capuchin monkeys. The first column represents the "actors," or groomers, and the remaining columns represent the "recipients," or the groomees. The diagonal is filled with a null indicator for that cell because an individual cannot be actor and recipient. To make the matrix more readable and to increase the impact, the cells of the matrix should be "shuffled"

**Table 4.1    Total number of minutes of grooming time in a hypothetical group of capuchin monkeys (*Cebus capucinus*) over a study period.**

| Actor | Recipient | | | | |
| --- | --- | --- | --- | --- | --- |
| | Sally | Jane | Mary | Ed | Joe |
| Sally | — | 22 | 25 | 26 | 34 |
| Jane | 7 | — | 15 | 22 | 38 |
| Mary | 12 | 3 | — | 31 | 30 |
| Ed | 12 | 6 | 14 | — | 0 |
| Joe | 9 | 8 | 4 | 0 | — |

up and down by rows, then left and right by columns, such that the left side reflects a sequence of increasing or decreasing frequency as groomer. The net result of this activity provides a clear indication that, in this example, Sally does the most grooming, and Joe receives the most grooming. However, this is not always so clear as sometimes there is no distinct pattern.

An additional advantage of an interaction matrix is that it is simple to apply inferential statistical evaluation to one as it generally fulfills the expectations for chi-square analysis.

## Sociograms

Sociograms provide a way of visualizing observed social relationships within a network diagram that has been quantified using a matrix or other form of social measurement analyses (Rees 2015). Like the matrix, a sociogram is limited to the depiction of a particular subset of behaviors (usually one type of behavior per sociogram) observed within a study group. Individuals are represented by points or circles, and lines of varying thickness are based on a quantification of interactions that connect the points to represent the strength of the relationship, with arrows indicating the direction of the relationship. Reciprocal interactions may also be represented with arrowed lines. A first stage sociogram for grooming interactions within a particular group might look like the following illustration (Figure 4.2):

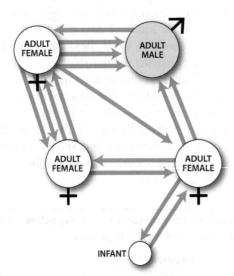

**Figure 4.2** Example of a sociogram. Each line with an arrow point represents several interactions.

It should be obvious that the repeated application of a line for each observed instance to indicate relationship interactions will rapidly become unreadable, and the meaningfulness of the diagram will be lost. The solution to this is to replace the groups of lines with a single, heavier line, often including a numerical value for the frequency or duration of the interactions in each direction, though this is not always necessary and may clutter the impact of the figure. Such a second-generation sociogram might look like Figure 4.3.

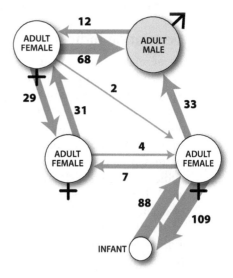

**Figure 4.3** Second generation sociogram example using proportional lines and numbers to indicate the extent of interactions between individuals.

Sociograms are also used occasionally to show probabilities of interrelationships between individuals or between specific classes of group members, but the calculation of such values is beyond the intention of this exercise. Interested students are referred to Altmann (1968) for this technique.

## Interaction Rates

A straightforward method of analyzing social relationships is by calculating rates of social interactions between two individuals. Such interactions can be *symmetric*, where there is no direction of interaction between two individuals (e.g., proximity rates per hour of observation for a given dyad), or *asymmetric*, where the interaction has an observable direction (e.g., the rate at which one individual grooms another).

Because calculating rates of interactions involves some number divided by another, it is important to pay attention to what number is being used in the denominator of the equation, or the total units of effort, as they can give different interaction rates. For example, in the equation below, $I_{AB}$ is the interaction rate for dyad $AB$, $n_{AB}$ is the number of interactions for dyad $AB$, and $e_{AB}$ is units of effort for dyad $AB$ (Whitehead 2008).

$$I_{AB} = \frac{n_{AB}}{e_{AB}}$$

Units of effort can be dependent on the sampling method. For focal animal sampling, for example, the units of effort may be the total time or sampling intervals where one of the two individuals in the dyad was sampled (Whitehead 2008). Ensure that you are not introducing bias when calculating the rates of interaction by choosing your denominator carefully.

## Association Indices

Social relationships can also be analyzed using any number of available association indices by inputting raw data on social interactions within dyads into an equation, which can elucidate the underlying social relationships among individuals in a group. Association indices are particularly useful when analyzing proximity, for example, as these are symmetric associations (but see below for an explanation of the maintenance of proximity). Most association indices are expressed as a proportion of time that two individuals spend in association (which is variously defined according to a particular study, but involves some valid distance measure); thus, they range from 0 to 1.0, with 0 reflecting no association time and 1.0 reflecting 100% association time.

Whitehead (2008) provides an overview of several popular association indices to use with comments on when they are most useful (reviewed in Table 4.2).

**Table 4.2   Commonly used association indices (adapted from Whitehead 2008).**

| Index | Formula | Comments |
|---|---|---|
| Simple ratio | $\dfrac{x}{x + y_{AB} + y_A + y_B}$ | Unbiased when assumptions* hold |
| Half weight | $\dfrac{x}{x + y_{AB} + 1/2(y_A + y_B)}$ | Most common; best when individuals more likely to be identified when not associated or not all associates identified |
| Twice weight | $\dfrac{x}{x + 2y_{AB} + y_A + y_B}$ | Best when individuals more likely to be identified when associated |
| Social affinity | $\dfrac{x}{\min\left[(x + y_{AB} + y_A), (x + y_{AB} + y_B)\right]}$ | Useful when individuals differ in identifiability |
| Both identified | $\dfrac{x}{x + y_{AB}}$ | Controls for co-occurrence |

*See Whitehead (2008:98) for list of assumptions; $x$ = number of sampling periods with $A$ and $B$ observed associated; $y_A$ = number of sampling periods with just $A$ identified; $y_B$ = number of sampling periods with just $B$ identified; $y_{AB}$ = number of sampling periods with $A$ and $B$ identified but not observed.

## Maintenance of Proximity

While on its surface proximity is considered a symmetrical association, further analysis using maintenance of proximity calculations, referred to as Hinde's Index (Hinde and Atkinson 1970), can reveal which individual in a given dyad is responsible for maintaining the relationship. Hinde's Index accounts for the proportion of approaches and leaves for each individual in the dyad, and uses the following equation:

$$\frac{APP_A}{APP_B + APP_A} - \frac{LEA_A}{LEA_B + LEA_A}$$

Where $APP_A$ is the number of approaches by individual $A$ toward individual $B$ and $APP_B$ is the number of approaches by individual $B$ toward $A$. $LEA_A$ is the number of leaves of individual $A$ toward individual $B$, and $LEA_B$ is the number of leaves of individual $B$ toward individual $A$ (Hinde and Atkinson 1970). The data are generally collected using focal animal sampling, and the calculated proportion represents which individual in the dyad is more responsible for maintaining the relationship; the higher the score, the more that individual is responsible for maintaining proximity within that dyad.

## Social Network Analysis

Increasingly, social network analysis is being used as a method of analyzing social relationships within groups or among individuals. Social network analysis uses networks and graph theory to elucidate social structures and has been employed in a wide range of disciplines for some time, but has only recently been applied to primate studies. Groups or subgroups are viewed as *networks* comprised of *nodes* (vertices or points, generally referring to individuals, but could be groups, units, or communities), and connected by *edges* that represent the social interactions (Whitehead 2008). In this sense, social network graphs are just sophisticated sociograms, but the associated analyses are more complicated. While increasingly popular in primatology, the scope of using social network analysis is beyond this book, and we refer the reader to an abundance of literature on the topic (e.g., Whitehead 2008; Coleing 2009; Kasper and Voelkl 2009; Brent et al. 2011; Seuer et al. 2011; Makagon et al. 2012; Scott and Stokman 2015).

## Computer Programs for Behavioral Analysis

The analyses of social behavior usually involve large sets of data; therefore, there are various types of computer programs available to assist with analyses. Some are specific to certain types of analyses, others are more general but able to handle behavioral data. Table 4.3 lists some software programs that may be useful for various types of social behavior analysis.

**Table 4.3    Software programs useful for primate social behavior analysis (adapted from Whitehead 2008).**

| Name | URL | Free? | Comments |
|---|---|---|---|
| Minitab | http://www.minitab.com/en-us/ | No | General statistical software |
| SPSS | https://www.ibm.com/products/spss-statistics | No | General statistical software |
| Systat | https://systatsoftware.com/ | No | General statistical & graphing software |
| SAS | www.sas.com/en_us/ | No | General statistical software |
| R | https://www.r-project.org/ | Yes | Extremely powerful statistics, analyses, & graphing software |
| JMP | https://www.jmp.com/en_us/home.html | No | General statistical & graphing software |
| Matlab | https://www.mathworks.com/products/matlab.html | No | General statistical software |
| GraphPad | https://www.graphpad.com/scientific-software/prism/ | No | General statistical & graphing software |
| XLSTAT | https://www.xlstat.com/en/ | No | General statistical & graphing software (pairs with Microsoft Excel) |
| Tableau | https://www.tableau.com/ | No | Data analysis & graphing software |
| OriginLab | https://originlab.com/ | No | General statistical & graphing |
| SOCPROG | http://whitelab.biology.dal.ca/SOCPROG/social.htm | Yes* | Wide range of social analysis |
| UCINET | http://www.analytictech.com/archive/ucinet.htm | No | Social network analysis |
| Pajek | http://mrvar.fdv.uni-lj.si/pajek/ | Yes | Social network analysis |
| Netdraw** | https://sites.google.com/site/netdrawsoftware/download | Yes | Social network graphing software |
| Graphviz | http://www.graphviz.org/ | Yes | Social network graphing software |
| iGraph | https://igraph.org/redirect.html | Yes | Social network graphing software |
| Gephi | https://gephi.org/ | Yes | Social network graphing software |
| Socnetv | https://socnetv.org/ | Yes | Social network analysis |

*SOCPROG is available in a compiled format that runs on its own, or with Matlab (which is not free) in a more powerful format.
**Can be downloaded separately or as part of UCINET.

# FIVE

# Biological and
# Morphological Sampling

It is common in primatology for behavioral data to be supplemented with biological or morphological data, such as hormone levels, parasite burdens, body size measurements (morphometrics), genetics, and others. Indeed, these types of data may even be presented without any behavioral data if this information can tell us something about the animal or the population. Those just starting in primatology may not collect biological or morphological data until they are proficient in behavioral data collection techniques, but this chapter is meant as an introduction to inform students of the types of information it is possible to gather and the level of invasiveness that may be necessary.

It is, of course, always preferable when data can be collected noninvasively. Researchers have worked for years to find valid ways of measuring certain variables using substances that animals excrete naturally, namely urine and feces. However, we are still limited for several measures that may require acquiring hair, saliva, blood, or tissues and often these substances require the animal to be captured and restrained. Body size measurements may also require restraint, though some novel techniques allow measures to be taken at a distance.

Below, we provide a table listing the types of physiological and biological data that are commonly collected in primate studies along with how you can obtain these types of data. We also provide a list of references that will be helpful if you want to investigate these types of data in more detail. This is followed by some tips on how to collect samples of different types. Students should be aware that this is not an exhaustive list of potential variables that could be measured (i.e., many hormones are not listed) and that new techniques are developed quickly, so a thorough search of the literature is, as always, necessary.

## Sample Collection: Tips and Logistical Constraints

Students should be aware that collection and storage protocols for biological samples can vary widely depending on the type of sample required and research questions addressed. All samples typically require specific types of collection tubes, mediums for storage, storage temperatures (from ambient room temperature to ultralow freezing temperatures), and methods of analyses that vary widely in their handling, protocol, level of expertise, and cost. These types of data analyses should not be undertaken without extensive research and proper validations. For example, if you are investigating hormones in urine or feces, it is usually not the actual hormone that is being excreted but, rather, some metabolite of the hormone. So, you would need to ensure that

**Table 5.1** Types of physiological and biological sampling in primates.

| Measure | Sample/ Measurement Type | Level of Invasiveness | Useful References |
|---|---|---|---|
| **Hormones** | | | |
| Review papers | | | Hodges and Heistermann 2003; Heistermann 2010; Higham 2016; Behringer and Deschner 2017; Ziegler and Crockford 2017 |
| Androgens | Blood | High | Sapolsky 1986 |
| | Urine | None | Robbins and Czekala 1997 |
| | Feces | None | Möhle et al. 2002 |
| | Saliva | Low | Shirtcliff et al. 2002 |
| Estrogens | Blood | High | Rinaldi et al. 2001 |
| | Urine | None | Hodges et al. 1979; Hodges and Eastman 1984 |
| | Feces | None | Heistermann et al. 1993 |
| | Saliva | Low | Czekala and Callison 1996 |
| Glucocorticoids | Blood | High | Sapolsky 1982 |
| | Urine | None | Turpeinen and Hämäläinen 2013 |
| | Feces | None | Bahr et al. 2000 |
| | Saliva | Low | Aardal and Holm 1995 |
| Progestins | Blood | High | Watanabe et al. 1990 |
| | Urine | None | Heistermann and Hodges 1995 |
| | Feces | None | Shideler et al. 1993; Fujita et al. 2001 |
| | Saliva | Low | DiGiano et al. 1992 |
| Oxytocin | Blood | High | Kramer et al. 2004 |
| | Urine | None | Crockford et al. 2013 |
| | Saliva | Low | McCullough et al. 2013 |
| Prolactin | Blood | High | Soltis et al. 2005 |
| | Urine | None | Soltis et al. 2005; Snowdon and Ziegler 2015 |
| **Parasites** | | | |
| Gastrointestinal | Feces | None | Gillespie 2006 |
| Blood-borne | Blood | High | Wolfe et al. 2002 |
| | Feces | None | Prugnolle et al. 2010 |
| Intracellular | Tissue | None (postmortem)– High | Gamble et al. 1996 |
| | Blood | High | Gamble et al. 2004 |
| Ectoparasites | Physical removal | High | Ancrenaz et al. 2003 |

*(continued)*

**Table 5.1** *(continued)*

| Measure | Sample/ Measurement Type | Level of Invasiveness | Useful References |
|---|---|---|---|
| **Microbiome** | | | |
| | Feces | None | Clayton et al. 2018; Blekhman et al. 2016 |
| | Skin | High | Council et al. 2016 |
| | Oral/rectal/ reproductive cavities | High | https:// www.primatemicrobiome.org/; https://hmpdacc.org/ |
| **Genetics** | | | |
| Review paper | | | Goossens et al. 2003 |
| DNA | Feces | None | Morin et al. 2001; Di Fiore 2003; Perry et al. 2010 |
| | Blood | Med.–High | Jeanpierre 1987 |
| | Tissue | None (postmortem)– High | Mason et al. 2016 |
| | Hair | None–High | Valderrama et al. 1999 |
| **Energetics** | | | |
| C-peptide | Urine | None | Emery Thompson and Knott, 2008 |
| Thyroid hormone* | Feces | None | Cristóbal-Azkarate et al. 2016 |
| **Morphometrics** | | | |
| *Living subjects* Bodyweight | Scale | None–High | Altmann and Alberts 1987; Brett et al. 1982 |
| Body measurements | Photos with scale bar | None | Mori 1979; Barrickman et al. 2015 |
| | Direct measure | High | Glander et al. 1992; King et al. 2011 |
| Muscle mass (creatinine) | Urine | None | Heymsfield et al. 1983 |
| *Dead subjects* | Direct measure | None | Groves and Harding 2003 |
| **Body condition** | | | |
| Coat condition | Scoring system | None | Berg et al. 2009 |

*There are currently some questions as to whether this is an accurate measure due to contrasting results with different species.

what you are measuring correlates with the hormone of interest. Thus, analyzing biological samples usually requires collaboration with experts that have laboratories dedicated to the type of analyses you are interested in.

It is also important to be aware of the potential for zoonotic disease transfer when dealing with nonhuman primate biological samples. When collecting these types of samples, proper personal protective equipment like latex gloves and face masks should always be worn, and analyses should be undertaken in laboratories with appropriate biosafety measures in place (see Centers for Disease Control and Prevention 2009; https://www.osha.gov/ for further information on this in the United States; and https://www.canada.ca/en/public-health/services/canadian-biosafety-standards-guidelines.html in Canada). If you are doing your analyses in a country other than these, you should check the regulations for biosafety in laboratories there.

In terms of biological sampling in the field, most researchers will likely be working with feces, urine, saliva, or hair, so we will focus on some practical tips for collection of these types of samples. If blood or tissues are needed, immobilization and capture would generally be required, and experienced personnel and veterinary support are essential for the health and welfare of the primate subjects and the researchers. Thus, capturing wild primates should never be undertaken without serious consideration (see Glander et al. 1991; Glander 1993; Larsen et al. 1999; Jolly et al. 2011; and Unwin et al. 2011 for information on capturing primates through anesthesia or other means).

Tissues can also (and probably should) be collected in the case of the death of a study subject if the body can be found. A useful guide for how to conduct a necropsy, or postmortem examination, in the field is freely available online from the Wildlife Conservation Society (Munson et al. 2006). If you are faced with having to conduct a necropsy, we recommend this resource or one like it be consulted. Additionally, if you are going to try to preserve the bones or other body parts and measure them, Groves and Harding (2003) provide an excellent guide. Below, we will also briefly touch on some body size and condition measurements that can be done in the field noninvasively.

For any type of biological sample, the labels that are put onto the vial, bag, or container for the sample usually include (we recommend the use of a permanent marker, like a Sharpie, to ensure the information is not lost):

- the date and time of sample collection;
- the group name;
- the age-sex class of the individual who provided the sample;
- the identity of the individual if known;
- where the sample was collected (e.g., a GPS point, or physical descriptions); and
- the name of the individual collecting the sample.

## Fecal Samples

Generally, fecal samples are the simplest samples to collect because they can just be picked up from the forest floor or substrate, wherever your study animals are located. For most analyses, it is important to know which animal the sample came from and to collect the feces soon after defecation. The way that samples are collected and stored is important depending on the type of information you wish to extract. Particularly for genetic samples, it is important not to contaminate the fecal sample with your own primate DNA when you collect it, so it is best to have your hair back, wear gloves and a face mask, and to pick up the sample with a sterile swab (ideally) or at least a clean spoon or stick. It is also important to ensure that where you touch the implement is not the same place that touches the feces. The vials and storage medium that you place fecal samples in after collection depend greatly on the analyses you wish to conduct, so we recommend you consult the literature for methods appropriate to your study.

It is important with fecal samples to be aware that whatever information you are trying to obtain from them is subject to some delay due to the length of the digestive process. For instance, the hormone metabolites that you are measuring may be representative of the hormones that were released in the blood the day before, but it took many hours for them to be excreted in the feces. Primate species vary in the duration of the digestive process. For example, colobine monkeys (and their multichambered stomachs) usually have a longer gut passage time than primates with single-chambered stomachs. If this information is not available in the literature for your study subjects, students can gauge how long the digestive process is by monitoring the diet of the animals and then collecting successive fecal samples to look for cues as to what was eaten (e.g., recognizable seeds, insect carapaces, and so on). This can give you the time from ingestion to excretion. For example, during her PhD research, Julie Teichroeb assessed the testosterone metabolites in the feces of colobus monkeys. The length of the digestive process was estimated when the monkeys ingested red soil and the time it took for the red coloration to appear in their normally green/brown feces was measured (Teichroeb and Sicotte 2008).

## Urine Samples

Though useful for many biological measures, urine samples can be difficult to obtain, particularly in the field. Luckily, often a small volume is needed for analyses so even if only a few drops can be collected, it may be enough. The substrate that your study animals are on is key to how easily urine samples can be collected. Urine can be pipetted off solid surfaces or off large leaves if it pools. In areas where the animals are on bare ground, it may be impossible to collect urine as it is immediately absorbed into the soil. However, when the primates are up in trees, urine can be caught as it falls in a bag (sometimes stretched over a net) or large funnel, but this is difficult to do. Plastic tarps can also be placed on the ground to allow urine to be pipetted off after it falls, but as you can imagine, it is hard to know where and when an animal will urinate.

Once again, it is important to know which animal the sample came from and to collect the sample immediately. As with feces, there is a delay for hormones released in the body to be excreted in the urine but this is typically not long. For example, in mice, injected corticosterone was detected in urine 2 hours after injection compared to feces, where it was detected 10 hours afterward (Touma et al. 2003).

## Saliva Samples

Collecting these types of samples involves getting the animals to chew on a swab for enough time to allow it to soak up some saliva before the researcher puts the swab into a vial. While this can often be done with captive animals, it is difficult with wild animals. Even for captive animals, the process can be tricky because species and individuals vary a great deal in how willing they are to chew on a swab. Typically, the swab must be baited or soaked in a tasty substance, which can sometimes interfere with later analyses. In the wild, provisioned animals or those used to taking food from human sources, such as refuse dumps, can sometimes be given swabs soaked in a sugar solution to chew on until they discard them, allowing the researcher to collect them (e.g., Higham et al. 2010).

However, if animals are not willing to chew on a swab, getting saliva may be impossible without immobilization and capture using anesthetic drugs. Many hormones released in the blood appear almost instantaneously in the saliva (reviewed in Kirschbaum and Hellhammer 1989; Vining and McGinley 1986), making data gained from these samples useful for associating with current behavior and social situations.

## Hair Samples

Similar to saliva samples, hair samples can usually be collected from captive animals but can be difficult to get from wild animals. Even for captive animals, immobilization or sedation may be necessary unless you are content with hair that the animals lose naturally. The benefit of hair for hormone analyses is that it gives you hormone values over time (however long it took for the hair to grow) (reviewed in Fourie and Bernstein 2011). Hair can also give you genetic samples, particularly if the bulb of root is attached (Gagneux et al. 1997).

Given that it can be collected without the researcher being present and can be a good way to survey secretive animals, many inventive methods of collecting hair have been attempted, including sticky darts shot at animals, hair traps made of barbed wire, hook-and-loop strips, roofing nails, and other mechanical means (Valderrama et al. 1999; Castro-Arellano et al. 2010). Hair traps work best for animals that can be baited to rub on a surface using scent, so these could be promising for strepsirrhines but are unlikely to work well for haplorhines. From a practical perspective, it is also easier for researchers to set up hair traps closer to the ground than high up in a forest canopy, so they may be more effective for use in terrestrial or semiterrestrial primates versus strictly arboreal primates.

## Body Size Measurements

*Body weight* is a measure that is often of interest because it can tell you a lot about the overall health of an animal, but it is difficult to get accurate weights on wild primates without anesthetizing animals (King et al. 2011). Captive animals can often be trained to step on scales for regular weight readings, while wild animals can be lured onto scales with bait if they take human food sources and it is permitted to give them food (Uehara and Nishida 1987; Pusey et al. 2005). Body weights have also been successfully recorded by placing scales near study groups without bait. The fact that it is a novel object causes the animals to investigate it, allowing researchers to record their weight when they are alone on top of it (Altmann and Alberts 1987). These methods have been successfully used with more terrestrial primates, but the challenges posed by having primarily arboreal study species or those that are not easily tempted by human food have yet to be overcome, to our knowledge.

*Body size* measurements can also be obtained without sedation. Photographs of the animals can be used but the researcher must include some known scale bar in the photo to allow comparison. For semiterrestrial species, measurements have been successfully taken by placing a large ruler in a certain spot and photographing animals as they pass by the ruler (Mori 1979). For arboreal (and terrestrial) species, a parallel laser device can be attached to a camera that projects a scale bar of known length somewhere on the animal or a surface near the animal so that it appears in the photo (Rothman et al. 2008; Barrickman et al. 2015). However, it is important that the lasers are projected in the same plane as the body part being measured, and laser devices can be finicky in the field. For example, Julie Teichroeb's research team recently used this technique and found it difficult to keep the lasers perfectly parallel over the day. They tended to shift during field work so that the scale bar being projected was no longer consistent at all distances from the device. To account for this, the distance between the laser points was checked after each photo session at the exact distance that the photographed monkey was located so that the length of the scale bar was known exactly (Teichroeb et al. 2020). This was time-consuming but did provide valid results.

Direct body measurements on primates generally require immobilization (see Glander et al. 1992 for definitions of typical body measurements), and can be obtained using flexible measuring tapes and/or retractable tape measures. The most important aspect of obtaining measurements on sedated primates is to ensure consistency in how each measurement is obtained; therefore, specific methodological definitions, and having the same person conducting measurements or training students, are preferable.

## Body Condition

Measures of stress hormones and levels of parasitism can give you important data on animal health; however, researchers have also come up with ways to score coat and tail condition noninvasively (e.g., Berg et al. 2009). These can be accurate and valid as long as body condition is assessed systematically, though it may also be best if the same observer scores animals over time to minimize individual differences between researchers.

# SIX

# A Statistical Primer

"There are lies, damned lies, and then there are statistics!" This famous quote, sometimes attributed to Mark Twain, is the byword of many students, but it need not be so. Basic statistical concepts are among the most favored skills of modern society and help one make sense of the world, but the practical application of statistics is something that is not always taught. This chapter is intended to demystify statistics. It will present the student with the practical utility of a basic statistical understanding to aid in the completion of the observational and field exercises presented in this book.

Statistics is the branch of mathematics that deals with data collection, analyses, interpretation, and presentation, so it is vital to any observational study. Statistics are normally divided into two large categories: *descriptive* and *inferential*. We will focus mostly on descriptive statistics in this overview with some reference to how you can choose the right inferential statistics to suit your data. Descriptive statistics do what the label applied to them suggests, they "describe" the characteristics and features of the data set. They decrease the seeming chaos of a large data set and begin to make your results digestible and understandable. Descriptive statistics should be explored and considered before moving on to inferential statistics because an extensive mass of information can be simply extracted through their use. Note, however, that descriptive statistics do not allow hypothesis testing; this is the realm of inferential statistics.

In contrast to descriptive statistics, inferential statistics "infer" from a sample what the conditions of a larger population are likely to be. They involve probabilistic statements such as "survey results are accurate to plus or minus 3 percent, 19 times out of 20." This is basically stating that we think the results we have found from this sample are accurate to within a range of plus and minus 3 points and would be so in 19 samples if we repeated the process on 20 samples. Inferential statistics thus are used to infer or make predictions about other samples, but these tests can also be used to make a mathematical assessment of the validity of the data collected.

## Descriptive Statistics

Our coverage of descriptive statistics will not be like a standard text, it will look at two main categories—measures of distribution and simple comparative statistics—without any attempt at developing or supporting relevant theories, and will then deal with the issues of data table construction and the use of Excel or statistics programs to mechanize the process. Coverage will proceed with a sequence of terms, some discussion of them, and example calculations based on simple data sets.

# Basic Terms

Some of the most important terms related to statistical analyses of behavior are those that divide the data into types. The data collected dictates how the statistical description and analyses will be done, and what measures can be employed.

**Qualitative data:** Descriptive data that are nonnumerical. An example would be the description of an infanticide event.

**Quantitative data:** Measurable data that can be numerically expressed and verified. Examples would be height or weight.

Qualitative data collection can capture some things more easily than quantitative data collection methods, such as concepts, interview responses, or sequences of rare behaviors. However, analyzing and interpreting such data can be difficult because these are often subjective. Analysis of qualitative data usually involves organizing the data, forming groups based on a predetermined structure, and looking for patterns. With the exception of rare behaviors, most data collected in primatology are quantitative and the statistical methods we cover here are applied to these data types.

Other important definitions you must remember for this chapter are those of *event* vs. *state*, which were covered in chapter 2. Recall that events are behaviors without a measurable duration, whereas states are durational behaviors. The term "bout" is often used informally in conjunction with these categories even though it has specific definitions that need to be clearly indicated in the context of their use.

**Bout**: Most often used to refer to a sequence of related durational behaviors. For instance, the interchange of grooming between two partners, where A grooms B five times and B grooms A three times, all occurring within a short period without other behaviors intervening, may be called a "grooming bout." It may also be used to refer to the frequency of durational behaviors (e.g., "12 grooming bouts occurred during the 6-hour period.").

An alternative when using short interval scans involves counting the strings of observations, a bout consisting of a sequence of uninterrupted behavior records that are the same, i.e., if the record looks like:

1-grm
2-grm
3-feed
4-grm
5-grm
6-feed

There would be "two bouts of grooming and two of feeding" despite there being four records of grooming. The assumption when the intervals between observations are short is that the behavior has been continuous and thus it constitutes a single behavioral string.

The next three terms are often related to the differentiation of event from state data, in that event data are considered to have no duration, and it is general practice to ignore transition times. These may be of importance when data are being extracted from video or acoustic records with a fine-grained analytical technique such as frame-by-frame analysis. Frequency is applicable to both event and state data, but is without a time factor associated.

**Duration:** The measurable time over which a behavior takes place.

**Transition time:** The finite period taken by a subject to change from one state to another, or alternatively the onset or termination of a behavior.

**Frequency:** The number of occurrences of a behavior—either events or the beginning of state behaviors may be counted. Note that no time period is involved. This is also known as the "raw count."

## The Example Data Sets

A small sample of data is employed in the following series of statistical operations to provide examples of how the calculations may be employed and interpreted. Two behavioral patterns are included from a study of olive baboons: sexual mounting and roar-grunt vocalizations. The definitions of these are not relevant to their use as examples, nor should these data be cited as valid.

1. Sexual mounting is observed 100 times in a study of 400 minutes duration divided into 15-minute sampling units or periods. The total duration of this behavior was 123 minutes and the group had twelve members.

2. Roar-grunts were recorded 146 times in a total sample of 3,794 behavioral occurrences and accounted for 378 minutes out of the 23,459 minutes in the study.

## Measures of Central Tendency and Dispersion

Two issues are always relevant in any statistical analysis: how the data are distributed, and the measures of central tendency. These statistics outline the distributional characteristics of a data set. We will begin with measures of central tendency.

**Mean or Average:** This normally implies the *arithmetic mean*, and it is produced by summing all the individual observations and dividing the total by the number of observations. Means are calculated as part of the standard deviation example below.

**Median:** The value of the variable in an ordered array or sequence that has an equal number of items on either side of it. If the data are arranged in ascending or descending order, the median represents the midpoint of the distribution.

**Mode:** The most commonly occurring value in a distribution. For instance, the value of the grade achieved by the greatest number of individuals in a class. If there are two values that both occur equally most often, the distribution is said to be *bimodal*, and if there are more than two values that occur an equally high number of times it is *multimodal*.

The best measure of central tendency to use is dependent on the data set. These three measures may coincide at the same value on a symmetrical (or Gaussian) curve, like the curve representing a normal distribution. The mode is the only measure of central tendency that can be used with both categorical and numerical data; however, it doesn't always represent the midpoint of the data well. The mean is probably used most frequently, but it is the most affected by skewed distributions and outliers, which are data points that are atypical or extreme compared to the rest of the data. For this reason, many scientists maintain that the median is the best measure.

Measures of central tendency show the values in a data set that are most frequent, while measures of dispersion are used to describe the spread of the data or its variation around a central value. We will focus on two simple and commonly used measures of dispersion.

**Range:** The highest and lowest scores of any measure. The range reflects the outside limits of the data but says nothing about how the rest of the data are distributed.

**Standard deviation:** The standard deviation is the most commonly used measure of dispersion and it measures the degree to which values are spread away from the mean. It is defined as the square root of the squared deviations of the scores around the mean, divided by the number of scores.

## A Standard Deviation Calculation and Example

The formula for the standard deviation is:

$$s.d. = \sqrt{\frac{\sum d^2}{N-1}}$$

where *d* is the deviation of an individual value from the mean, $\sum$ (sigma) is the symbol for "sum of," and *N* is the number of cases. The formula can be read as: "the standard deviation of the sample equals the square root of the value yielded by the sum of squares of the deviations divided by the number of cases minus one." The "sum of squares of the deviations of the measurements from the mean measurement" is necessary to this calculation and the formula for it is:

$$\sum d^2 = \sum x^2 - \frac{\left(\sum x\right)^2}{N}$$

where $x$ is each measurement value. Below is a step-by-step example of how to calculate these statistics.

You will need to obtain the following:

1. The sum of the measurements (i.e., add up all the individual measurement values, the $x$'s, this is $\sum x$).

2. The sum of the squares of the measurements (i.e., square each measurement and then add up all those values $= \sum x^2$).

3. The square of the sum of the measurements $= (\sum x)^2$.

4. The sum of squares of the deviations of the measurements from the mean, the last formula given above $= \sum d^2$.

An appropriate format for calculating these measures is a table of your data setup as follows (Note: Do not round off any values until the end of your calculations; rounding at an earlier stage will lead to inaccuracies in your calculation):

| Measurement # | (x values) | $x^2$ values |
|---|---|---|
| 1 | 10.000 | 100 |
| 2 | 10.016 | 100.320256 |
| 3 | 9.997 | 99.940009 |
| 4 | 9.991 | 99.820081 |
| 5 | 10.023 | 100.460529 |
| 6 | 10.002 | 100.040004 |
| 7 | 9.998 | 99.960004 |
| 8 | 9.996 | 99.920016 |
| 9 | 10.011 | 100.220121 |
| 10 | 10.000 | 100 |

Add each column to get: $\sum x$ $\sum x^2$

- Sum of measurements: $\sum x = 100.034$
- Sum of squares of the measurements: $\sum x^2 = 1000.681020$
- Square of the sum of the measurements: $(\sum x)^2 = 0006.80116$
- Sum of squares of the deviations of the measurements from the mean:

$$\sum d^2 = \sum x^2 - \frac{\left(\sum x\right)^2}{N}$$

Insert the arithmetic values

$$\sum d^2 = 1000.681020 - \left( \frac{10006.80116}{10} \right)$$

$$= 1000.681020 - (1000.680116)$$

$$= 0.000904$$

Therefore, the Standard Deviation

$$= \sqrt{\frac{0.000904}{9}}$$

$$= \sqrt{0.0001004444} \text{ (recurring)}$$

$$= 0.01002219537$$

rounded to $SD = \pm 0.01$

# Frequencies and Rates

Some of the most basic calculations are founded on how often certain behaviors occur (i.e., frequency data or raw counts) over some period of time, or in relation to other behaviors.

**Relative frequency:** This indicates the probability of a particular behavior being observed at a randomly selected behavior change.

$$\frac{\text{Frequency of one behavior}}{\text{Total number of behavior changes}} = \text{Relative frequency}$$

**Example**

In a particular sample, the behavior of grooming another group member occurs 36 times within a total of 479 behavior changes (transitions from one behavior to another),

$$\frac{36 \text{ (behavior frequency)}}{479 \text{ (total behavior changes)}} = \text{relative frequency}$$

Thus, relative frequency $= 0.075$

Interpretation is straightforward: In the sample recorded, the probability of any behavior change involving a switch to "grooming" is 0.075.

**Rate:** A rate is the frequency per unit of time of any behavior or event. Rates are useful when making comparisons between species and populations because the data are standardized and thus directly comparable. Rates, of course, require that the duration of the sample be known. Having equal sample periods makes the calculation easier but the calculation is still valid with unequal durations if the total observation time is divided into the sum of the frequencies for all samples. Rates are most useful when a common time base, such as frequency per hour or per minute, is employed. Thus, there are two variants of the calculation.

Frequency per sample unit:

$$\frac{\text{Number of occurrences}}{\text{Number of time units}} = \text{Rate} \quad \text{(frequency per sample unit)}$$

Frequency per time unit:

$$\frac{\text{Number of occurrences}}{\text{Total observation time}} = \text{Rate} \quad \text{(frequency per hour or minute)}$$

In any presentation of a rate, it is obligatory to present the units involved.

**Example**
Sexual mounting is observed 100 times in a study of 400 minutes duration, which is divided into 15-minute sampling units (400 minutes equals 26.67 sample units). The rate of sexual mounting is thus

$$100/400 = 0.25 \text{ mounts per minute,}$$

or

$$100/26.67 = 3.75 \text{ mounts per sample period.}$$

**Hourly rate:** A variation of the rate calculation using "hours" as the time unit.

$$\frac{\text{Frequency of behavior}}{\text{Hours of observation}} = \text{Hourly rate}$$

**Example**
The sexual mounting data would yield an hourly rate of

$$100/6.67 \text{ hours} = 14.992 \text{ times per hour.}$$

Since the number of significant digits appropriate here is zero (i.e., mounts occur or not), the rate would be rounded to 15 per hour.

# Probability, Proportion, and Percentage

These three terms are all closely related and similar to the calculations for relative frequencies, though the context and use of these are different.

**Proportion:** The decimal expression of any fraction. The formula is essentially the same as for relative frequency, but the formula is also used with durations (time):

$$\frac{\text{Behavior A frequency (or duration)}}{\text{T (total frequency of all behaviors or durations)}} = \text{Proportion A of T}$$

### Example

Roar-grunts in a baboon field study were recorded 146 times in a total sample of 3,794 behavioral occurrences and continued for 378 minutes out of the 23,459 minutes.

Therefore, the proportion of behaviors that were roar-grunting (or the relative frequency of roar-grunting) was 146/3794 = 0.0384, and the proportion of time baboons spent roar-grunting was 378/23459 = 0.0161.

**Probability:** The proportional expression of the likelihood of a particular behavior occurring. This occurs on a scale of zero to one, with the maximum probability of 1.0 meaning that the behavior *always* occurs while a probability of 0.0 (the minimum) means that it *never* occurs.

### Example

In the baboon data set, the probability of hearing roar-grunts during any particular minute of the study is 0.0161. But a simpler, and more direct example is: if a study shows that during the hour from 9 to 10 o'clock 76 out of 100 students are seated at their desks, the probability of any one student being seated during that hour is 76/100 = 0.76.

**Percent:** The same calculation done for proportion but multiplied by 100 (i.e., a 0.76 proportion equals 76%).

---

# Comparative Statistics

The following calculations are more complex than the preceding have been, but they have a much greater utility in that they can be used to compare between groups and individuals. These calculations are inherently useful for describing and understanding the variation between individual primates and between larger aggregations such as groups or species.

**Mean duration per bout (MDB):** Total duration of a behavioral category divided by its frequency. This provides a measure of how long, on average, each behavior continues once it has begun.

$$\text{Mean duration of behavior A} = \frac{\text{Sum of durations of all A}}{\text{Total frequency of A}}$$

### Example

In the baboon sexual mounting data, the total duration of this behavior was 123 minutes, and mounts were observed 100 times. Therefore, the mean duration of each sexual mounting bout was 123/100 = 1.23 minutes (each mount takes an average of 1.23 minutes).

**Mean duration per hour (MDH):** The average number of minutes per hour in a state equals the total duration in minutes divided by the number of hours of observation. Note that the resulting units are "minutes per hour."

$$\text{Mean duration per hour of A} = \frac{\text{Sum of durations of A in minutes}}{\text{Total hours of observations}}$$

**Example**

For the baboon sexual mounting data, the mean duration per hour would be 123/6.67 = 18.44 minutes per hour.

**Mean duration per hour for scan sampling:** When interval sampling is used the difficulty lies in the calculation of the duration of the behaviors, and the not very precise relationship with real time. If a study results in 12,000 samples taken 10 seconds apart, the time involved is 12000 × 10 = 120,000 seconds = 2,000 minutes = 33.33 (recurring) hours. If a particular behavior is scored on 1289 samples, and we make the assumption that the record represents 10 seconds (the maximum possible) of that behavior, then the duration is 1289 × 10 = 12,890 seconds = 214.83 minutes = 3.58 hours. This behavior's mean duration per hour then is 214.83/33.33 = 6.446 minutes per hour.

**Mean rate per individual (MRI):** Total frequency for all individuals, divided by the total observation time for all individuals, all divided by the number of individuals in the study group. The resulting units become "occurrences per minute per individual." If the observation time is entered in hours, the units become "occurrences per hour per individual." This measure and the following one (MDI) are particularly useful when comparing across groups because the number of individuals (which typically differ between groups) is controlled.

$$\text{Mean rate of A per indiv.} = \frac{\left[\dfrac{\text{Total frequency of A for all indiv.}}{\text{Total observ. time (hours) for all indiv.}}\right]}{\text{Number of individuals}}$$

**Example**

For the sexual mounting data, since the group has twelve members, the mean rate per individual is 100/400 = 0.25 mounts per minute divided by 12 = 0.0208 mounts per minute per individual or 0.000346 mounts per hour per individual.

**Mean duration per individual (MDI):** Total duration for all individuals in minutes, divided by the total observation time for all individuals in hours, all divided by the number of individuals in the group. Resulting units for MDI are "minutes per hour per individual."

$$\text{Mean dur. of A per indiv.} = \frac{\left[\frac{\text{Total dur. (minutes) of A for all indiv.}}{\text{Total observ. time (hours) for all indiv.}}\right]}{\text{Number of individuals}}$$

### Example

For the sexual mount data, the group has 12 members, and the mean duration per individual is 123/6.67 = 18.440779 minutes per hour divided by 12 = 1.54 minutes per hour per individual.

An alternative mode of calculation for MRI and MDI, but only if the sample durations are equal for all subjects, involves using the individual mean rates (calculated as total frequency or duration for an individual divided by the observation time for the individual). These can be summed and divided by the number of individual subjects.

# Percentages of Time for Continuous and Interval Sampling Protocols

Amongst the most common calculations in primatology are those that attempt to show how the subjects allocate their time, especially when some comparison between populations, environments, or species is being undertaken. Because continuous and interval sampling produce distinctly different kinds of data, caution must be employed in selecting the correct calculation model.

**Percent of time for continuous sampling:** Often it is appropriate to calculate percentages of time as a preliminary to producing comparative tables or graphs of behaviors. For each behavior the calculation would be:

$$= \frac{\text{Mean duration per hour}}{60 \text{ minutes}} \times 100$$

### Example

For the sexual mounting data, where 123 minutes of 400 (6.67 hours) were observed in this activity, the percentage time would be (123/6.67)/ 60 × 100 = 30.73% of the time was taken up in sexual mounting.

**Percent of time for scan sampling:** It is often desired to calculate the percentage of "time" when using an interval sampling protocol; however, the result is a percentage of scans and is only an approximation of the percentage of real time. This technique has been investigated and the error rates for different intervals suggest that it represents real time best when scans are close together (ideally less than 10 seconds apart). However, if continuous sampling misses or misrepresents the duration of certain behaviors (e.g., in the wild, individuals are often lost during samples when they are moving), then scan sampling may be a better approximation of time spent in these behaviors.

$$= \frac{\text{Number of scans with behavior scored}}{\text{Total number of scans}} \times 100$$

| **Example**

In a scan sample study, 12,000 scans were taken at ten-second intervals, in 8,675 scans "resting" was recorded, and in 2,347 scans "locomotion" was recorded. The percent of time "resting" is 8675/12000 × 100 = 72.29%, and the percent of time "locomoting" is 2347/12000 × 100 = 19.56%. The caveat is that these are a percent of scans and not directly measured time.

## Statistical Reporting

In any report that employs statistical description of results, some tabular features are always appropriate and expected. The two main items are tables dealing with the frequency and duration data.

1. *Frequency table:* This should show the raw frequency and the rates for the behaviors being reported. An example of a basic frequency table is shown in Table 6.1

2. *Duration table:* This should show the durations of behaviors being reported unless the study employs interval samples with more than 10 seconds between records, in which case no duration table is expected.

**Table 6.1   Basic frequency for a study involving three age-sex classes.**

| Behavior | Adult Male | Adult Female | Juvenile | Total |
|----------|-----------|--------------|----------|-------|
| Resting | 54 | 32 | 8 | 94 |
| Feeding | 34 | 61 | 41 | 136 |
| Locomotion | 12 | 19 | 98 | 129 |
| Grooming | 0 | 118 | 7 | 125 |
| Playing | 3 | 0 | 135 | 138 |
| Total | 103 | 230 | 289 | 622 |

Note that one additional row and column (called the "marginals") are necessary components of every table. They provide totals for each row and each column. When constructing a table, the marginals are an important safety check. In adding up the total row or the total column, the number produced must be the same in each direction; otherwise, there is an error within the data presented. The data in the table also allows some interpretation simply through inspection. In Table 6.1 it should be evident that the juvenile engages in more frequent behavior than the adults, and that the female spends less time resting and more time feeding than the male. It also shows that while play behavior may be the most frequent activity (based on the total column), virtually all of it is done by the juvenile. Similarly, while grooming is prominent, the female performs most of the grooming, while the male performs none. Such information can be directly interpreted, and differences between age or sex classes and between different behaviors easily seen and presented.

A slightly more complex frequency table would look like Table 6.2 with the presentation of frequency and rate data. A difference exists in this table with respect to the information in the marginals: it is optional to add up the rates in the column totals row, and the row total should not be added at all. The reason for proceeding in this way should be obvious: if column totals for rates are in place, as with the bracketed values in Table 6.2, the only thing that they demonstrate is the overall rate of behavior for the category. The rates in the row totals column are not a sum from the rates in the other columns, they are calculated rates from the total frequency, which is a sum. If the exercise of adding the rate values for the marginals is undertaken, it will not be equal (sum of column totals = 124.4, sum of row totals = 41.51). One further feature of Table 6.2 is the presence of abbreviations in the table and the consequent necessity for a "key" or "legend" to explain them and present the units employed.

**Table 6.2    An example of a basic frequency/rate table (based on 5 hours observation on each subject).**

| Behavior | Adult Male | | Adult Female | | Juvenile | | Total | |
|---|---|---|---|---|---|---|---|---|
| | f | r | f | r | f | r | f | r |
| Resting | 54 | 10.8 | 32 | 6.4 | 8 | 1.6 | 94 | 6.26 |
| Feeding | 34 | 6.8 | 61 | 12.2 | 41 | 8.2 | 136 | 9.06 |
| Locomotion | 12 | 2.4 | 19 | 3.8 | 98 | 19.6 | 129 | 8.66 |
| Grooming | 0 | 0 | 118 | 23.6 | 7 | 1.4 | 125 | 8.33 |
| Playing | 3 | 0.6 | 0 | 0 | 135 | 27 | 138 | 9.2 |
| **Total** | **103** | (20.6) | **230** | (46.0) | **289** | (57.8) | **622** | |

f = raw count, r = rate in occurrences per hour

Duration tables are similar in construction but hold different data. Table 6.3 presents some duration data and relevant calculations performed with the data. The data available for Table 6.3 allows the calculation of MDH for the three cases of the adult male, the adult female, and the totals, but note once again that calculations such as MDH, MDI, and percent of time may not be summed from the body of the table, nor will they yield the same values for row and column totals. The addition of the MDI calculation provides a value that would be of use in a comparative examination of the differences between this

**Table 6.3    An example of a basic duration table employing data on one male and one female.**

| Behavior | Adult Male | | | | Adult Female | | | | Total | | | | |
|---|---|---|---|---|---|---|---|---|---|---|---|---|---|
| | f | dur | MDH | % time | f | dur | MDH | % time | f | dur | MDH | MDI | % time |
| Resting | 54 | 178 | 35.6 | 59.3 | 32 | 41 | 8.2 | 13.7 | 86 | 219 | 21.9 | 10.9 | 36.5 |
| Feeding | 34 | 43 | 8.6 | 14.3 | 61 | 50 | 10.0 | 16.7 | 95 | 93 | 9.3 | 4.6 | 15.5 |
| Locomotion | 12 | 57 | 11.4 | 19.0 | 19 | 12 | 2.4 | 4.0 | 31 | 69 | 6.9 | 3.4 | 11.5 |
| Grooming | 0 | 0 | 0 | 0 | 118 | 197 | 39.4 | 65.7 | 118 | 197 | 19.7 | 9.8 | 32.8 |
| Playing | 3 | 0 | 4.4 | 7.3 | 0 | 0 | 0 | 0 | 3 | 22 | 2.2 | 1.1 | 3.7 |
| **Total** | **103** | 300 | 60 | 99.9 | **230** | 300 | 60 | 99.9 | 333 | 600 | 60 | 30 | 99.9 |

5 hours (300 minutes) observation on each individual; f = raw count; dur = duration in minutes; MDH = mean duration/hour in min/hour; MDI = mean duration per individual in min/hour/indiv

and another group of individuals. If MDI was calculated for the individual male and female in this case, it would equal the MDH. Such would not be the case if several members of each class were aggregated in the table.

Spreadsheet programs, such as Excel, can be set up in a relatively simple fashion to construct tables and perform the relevant calculations by copying and pasting formulas down and across columns. This can save a lot of time compared to completing calculations by hand. Most word processors, like Microsoft Word, can construct tables and even format them for presentations, though for presentations, tables can also be made directly in Microsoft PowerPoint.

# Inferential Statistics: Choosing the Right Tests

Recall in chapter 2, when we discussed research design, we introduced hypothesis testing. Hypothesis testing is also sometimes called "significance testing." Inferential statistics provide the tools to allow you to "reject" or "fail-to-reject" the hypotheses that you propose when beginning your study. There are many useful guides and websites available to help you in running inferential statistics, so here we are going to focus on how to choose appropriate tests.

The first step is determining what your dependent and independent variables are and their format. *Dependent variable(s)* are also known as outcome variables and are those that are being tested or measured. *Independent variables* (also referred to as "predictor variables") are those that change or are controlled and you can test their effects on the dependent variable. For example, if you were interested in the effects of temperature and rainfall on resting time in your study animals, resting time would be your dependent variable and temperature and rainfall would be your independent variables.

The nature and number of your dependent variable(s) are particularly important to choose the most suitable statistical test. Two things must be considered regarding your dependent variable:

1. At what level were the data for that variable collected or measured? Do your data consist of categories that cannot be ordered (nominal), ordered categories (ordinal), equally spaced values with no true zero (interval), or continuous values with a true zero (ratio)? You can refer back to chapter 2 to for explicit definitions of these categories.

2. How are the data distributed? We will cover the ways to determine data distributions below.

## Determining Data Distributions

Once you have determined the level at which your dependent variable was collected, you need to determine how the data are distributed. This is key to deciding which statistical tests are appropriate. The distribution refers to a list or a graph that shows all the values in your data set and how often each occurs. There are many different types of distributions possible (e.g., binomial, Gaussian or normal, Poisson, gamma, exponential, etc.). As an example, if your dependent variable is categorical but binary in that it has only two options (e.g., present or absent, success or failure) that you could represent with a 1 for present and a 0 for absent, you will have a *binomial distribution*. If, on the other hand, your data are continuous, graphs are particularly useful for determining the shape of the distribution because you will be able to see how your values plot out. You should create a histogram with all the values measured in your data set in chronological order on the x-axis, plotted against the frequency that each value occurs on the y-axis, as is shown below with a sample data set on grooming bout durations in a primate group (Figure 6.1). Here, grooming bout durations are binned in 30-second intervals to make viewing their distribution easier.

Many statistical tests require that the data in your dependent variable approach a Gaussian or "normal distribution." This is the classic bell-shaped curve (Figure 6.2) that large data sets often lead to. Remember that your data are always a sample drawn from the larger population. So, the larger the sample you manage to acquire, the more likely it is that the data will approach a normal distribution. In our histogram example, the data do not appear to be normally distributed; but there are statistical tests available that can tell you for certain whether the data are normally distributed, or not, in cases where you are unsure. Two examples are the Kolmogorov-Smirnov test and the Shapiro-Wilk test for which online calculators are available.

Once you have confirmed or rejected the normality of your dependent variable, you can consider the statistical tests that are valid for your data set (Table 6.4). A normally distributed dependent variable will allow you to run *parametric* tests, which have a lot of power and make it likely that you will detect a significant effect if it exists. However, there is no need to worry if your dependent variable is not normally distributed as there are nonparametric versions of most tests. *Nonparametric* tests are distribution-free because they do not assume that your data are distributed in a particular way. While parametric tests compare means, nonparametric tests compare medians. If the median is the best measure of central tendency for your data, you may want to use nonparametric tests, even if your data meet the requirements of parametric tests. Below is a table that will be helpful in determining which statistical tests you can use.

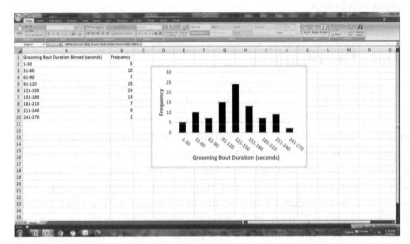

**Figure 6.1**
Example of how to produce a histogram.

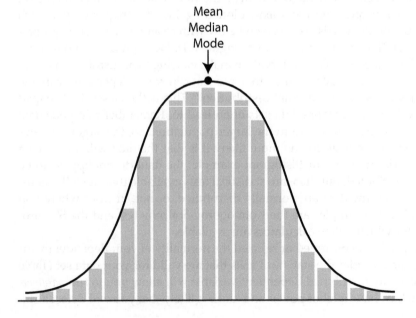

**Figure 6.2** The normal curve.

**Table 6.4 Guide for choosing the appropriate statistical test.**

| Goal | Dependent variable level of measurement | Distribution | Best test |
|---|---|---|---|
| Comparison of one group to a hypothetical value | Nominal | | Chi-square or Binomial test |
| | Ordinal | Non-normal | Wilcoxon test |
| | Ratio or Interval | Normal | One-sample t-test |
| | | Non-normal | Wilcoxon test |
| Comparison of two paired groups | Nominal | | McNemar's test |
| | Ordinal | Non-normal | Wilcoxon test |
| | Ratio or Interval | Normal | Paired t-test |
| | | Non-normal | Wilcoxon test |
| Comparison of two unpaired groups | Nominal | | Fisher's test |
| | Ordinal | Non-normal | Mann-Whitney test |
| | Ratio or Interval | Normal | Unpaired t-test |
| | | Non-normal | Mann-Whitney test |
| Comparison of three or more matched groups | Nominal | | Cochrane Q |
| | Ordinal | Non-normal | Friedman test |
| | Ratio or Interval | Normal | Repeated measures ANOVA |
| | | Non-normal | Friedman test |
| Comparison of three or more unmatched groups | Nominal | | Chi-square test |
| | Ordinal | Non-normal | Kruskal-Wallis test |
| | Ratio or Interval | Normal | One-way ANOVA |
| | | Non-normal | Kruskal-Wallis test |
| Measure of the association between two variables | Nominal | | Contingency coefficients |
| | Ordinal | Non-normal | Spearman correlation |
| | Ratio or Interval | Normal | Pearson correlation |
| | | Non-normal | Spearman correlation |
| Prediction from another measured variable | Nominal | | Simple logistic regression |
| | Ordinal | Non-normal | Nonparametric regression |
| | Ratio or Interval | Normal | Simple linear regression |
| | | Non-normal | Nonparametric regression |
| Prediction from several measured or binomial variables | Nominal or Ordinal | | Binary, Mulitnomial, or Ordinal logistic regressions |
| | Ratio or Interval | | Multiple linear regressions or Multiple nonlinear regressions |

A final note: Students should be aware that in primatology, data often do not meet the basic assumptions of statistical tests due to issues such as small sample sizes or repeated observations on the same individuals (called "non-independent samples"), and often more sophisticated statistical tests are needed (e.g., multivariate statistics, mixed models). Do not be afraid to consult with a statistician (most universities offer free statistics help in their math and statistics departments) or to use online statistics forums to ask for advice. These references may also prove useful: Siegel and Castellan (1988) for nonparametric statistics; Tabachnick and Fidell (2007) for multivariate statistics; and McCulloch and Searle (2001) and Bolker et al. (2009) for mixed models.

## Selecting a Level of Significance and Potential Errors

With inferential statistics, you are able to test your null hypothesis. However, you have to decide on the cutoff point that you feel is valid to reject the null hypothesis and find support for the alternative hypothesis. This value is referred to as *alpha* (α) or as the *p-value*. Alpha is the probability that the given hypothesis is true. The choice of alpha is arbitrary but there is a convention in many scientific disciplines, including primatology, to use p = 0.05 as the cut off for rejecting the null hypothesis. There is also a convention for using *two-tailed tests*. This means that the probability of the given result must fall in one of the two tails of the distribution. Alternatively, the test statistic falls within the area of 0.025 in either tail of the curve (so that the total area of acceptance is 0.025 + 0.025 = 0.05). Performing a *one-tailed test* at an alpha level of 0.05 means that you are predicting the direction of the result when testing the null hypothesis and that your test's statistic must fall in the 0.05 area under one side of the

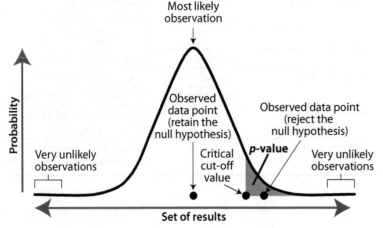

**Figure 6.3** An example of the alpha value in a one-tailed test. For a two-tailed test, a smaller area under both tails of the curve would allow the null hypothesis to be rejected.

A *p*-value (shaded area under the curve) is the probability of an observed (or more extreme) result arising by chance

curve. It is generally more conservative to perform two-tailed tests, which explains the convention in most disciplines.

In any statistical testing, there is the potential for making an error in your final conclusions. There are two main types of error that may occur:

1. **Type I error:** Also referred to as a "false positive." In this type of error, a true null hypothesis has been rejected incorrectly and an effect has been detected that is not actually present. The risk of making a type I error is denoted by alpha. At $p = 0.05$, there is a 5% chance of making a type I error.

2. **Type II error:** Also referred to as a "false negative." In this type of error, a false null hypothesis has been incorrectly retained. An effect is present but it has not been detected. This risk of committing a type II error is equal to one minus the power of the test (denoted by beta $\beta$).

For any data set, alpha and beta are traded off against one another. So, if you make your alpha level very small to decrease the chances of making a type I error, this increases your chances of making a type II error. The only way to decrease the odds of making both types of error is to increase the sample size. Note that statistical programs are necessary to run all but the simplest statistical tests. See chapter 9 for more discussion on helpful data organization and analysis programs.

# SEVEN

# The Preparation of Scientific Reports
## A Beginner's Guide

# Expectations for a Student Report

Scientific reporting varies a great deal. Reports may be terse, full of jargon, and essentially incomprehensible except to another specialist in the particular subfield, or they may be exceptionally fine literature. At either extreme, however, they will tend to follow the generalized format detailed in the following pages. For a student involved with the study of primates, the expectations are similar in that what is expected is a literate essay organized in the scientific report format, with sufficient tables, graphs, and/or figures to illustrate the text. It is expected that a student will conduct some examination of library resources in addition to performing observations, and must cite and reference the materials used. The citation mode expected in primatology varies but is often one of the APA (American Psychological Association) formats simply designated as Author-Date in the text (page numbers are only included for direct quotes). The pattern may be illustrated as:

> "As Smith and Jones (1893) found in their study of rabbitoes, the first action is a lateral bend . . ."

or

> "Male baboons weigh between 40 and 55 pounds (18 to 25 kilos) when captured in the wild" (DeVore and Washburn, 1963).

Very few primatology journals make use of footnotes, and the general direction is to avoid them. It is typically the case that one or more citations are provided for all factual statements that are not common knowledge. Every publication cited in the text of a paper or report must make an appearance in the bibliographic listing at the end of the document. It is of little real concern whether that component is labeled as References, Sources, Citations, or Bibliography. What matters is the consistent use of the same format throughout, and complete referencing of all cited, borrowed, quoted, or paraphrased materials used in the generation of the report. Several bibliographic programs are available for all major computer platforms to scan a document and generate a full reference listing. They are usually able to produce it in several different formats. A note of caution: These software types often produce a reference listing full of errors and inconsistencies, so the author must go through and edit the list. However, just having the text in place is helpful and saves time.

Every report is expected to be presented with competent and correct grammar. Thus, it is important to proofread the document and correct the spelling and grammar before submission. A great place to start is the spelling and grammar checking modules available in your word processing software. Using these tools, students should be able to submit a well-written document. Good writing skills can be learned by anyone and mastered with practice.

# Writing for Primatology: Guidelines for the Scientific Report

Scientific reports in primatology follow the more or less standard pattern of Introduction, Methods, Results, Discussion, and Conclusion (sometimes referred to as the "IMRaD model," where the "a" denotes a subsection on how the data were analyzed). Also, there will often be illustrative material in the form of tables, graphs, and figures, perhaps appendices with explanatory material or data lists, and a bibliography. Table 7.1 provides a list of the important elements of each section of a scientific report in primatology: introduction, literature review, methods, results, discussion, conclusion, and references.

## Introduction

Contrary to most writers' practice, the introduction should be written as the last component of a report, once everything else is complete. The introduction leads the reader to the problem, theme, and content of the report. The problem, or research question, needs to be put into the context of the discipline, showing why it is important and worthy of investigation. This is often done by summarizing the work that has been done on the topic in the past. It is essential for an introduction to cogently present the reason for undertaking the project. This does not normally include "because it was required for the course," a truism that need not be repeated.

Within the introduction, the study species is usually introduced and the author explains why it is an appropriate model in which to address the research question. Finally, introductions often end with the hypotheses that are tested within the rest of the document (Table 7.1). Some, but not all, introductions end with a brief summary of what the results of the investigation were. The introduction presents the problem and how it was approached. It must encourage the reader to see the importance of the rest of the document and lead smoothly into the next sections.

## Literature Review

One point that separates a research paper from a thesis is the literature review—it is not considered to be a formal requirement in a research article but is normally part of a master's or doctoral thesis or dissertation. Literature reviews may take different forms but are generally seen as an extensive discussion of the relevant publications linked to the theory and data surrounding the issues that are central to the thesis. They are often typified by long strings of citations of works listed as supporting or denying support for each hypothesis, or providing comparative data about a species, ecosystem, habitat, and so on. For a beginning student of primatology, it is only necessary to be able to recognize the need for and characteristics of a literature review, though it will be important to learn more if the instructor decides that one is a necessary component of a report.

## Methods

This portion of a scientific report is where the author describes the population, the set of materials that were used in the study, and how the study was conducted. This does not necessarily have to be a deadly dull listing such as "32 subjects of *Macaca fuscata* were subjected to training for 10 trails followed by two test sessions in a standard Skinner enclosure." It can and should be written in a literate and engaging style. To inform the reader adequately of the scientific procedure employed in the study, the report needs to present sufficient details about the subject animals and their habitats, the study location and the dates/times the study took place, the methods employed in the study, and the duration or amount of data collected with each method. It is important to describe the makeup of the social group in terms of their age and sex composition, their habitat or enclosure, and any special conditions. In behavioral studies, the dominance rank (if known) of each study subject may also be required. These data may be conveniently presented as a table.

In this section, it is important to specify what observational procedure was employed, what the observing and recording protocols were, and any special rules used by the observer in the handling of the data. Where summarization and statistics (including graphs) are presented, the analytical mechanisms and programs used should be noted (Table 7.1). This is often done in a separate data analyses section at the end of the methods. The essence of this section is informing the reader what was done, who and where the subjects were, and how it was done. The reader should be able to judge the scientific validity of the study from this section alone. Enough information should be presented so that anyone wanting to replicate the study would be able to do so.

## Results

This section is where the analyses of the data are presented. While there is no precise statement of what this section must or must not contain, it is important to recognize that a complete listing of the raw data is not to be presented. The results section is expected to be a written component pointing out the important features and findings in the data. The results are often the worst prepared component of a student report. It is not sufficient to direct the reader to look at Tables 1 through 37 and Graphs 1 to 16. The results and observations should consist of summarizations of the observations, condensed descriptive statistical presentations, and perhaps a few notations of exceptional or unusual observa-

**Table 7.1    Summary of the most important information in each section of a scientific report.**

| Section | Information Included |
|---------|---------------------|
| Introduction | —Background on the research topic<br>—Clear statement of the research question<br>—Background on the study species (Why is it appropriate to answer the research question?)<br>—Set of hypotheses or predictions |
| Methods | —Where and when the study was conducted<br>—Information on the study group/population<br>—The sampling schedule and data collection methods<br>—How the data were analyzed |
| Results | —Summary of what was found with illustrative materials and statistical tests where appropriate |
| Discussion | —Explanation of how the results relate to previously published literature<br>—Was an answer to the research question found?<br>—Which hypotheses/predictions were supported and which were not?<br>—Why does the author think these results were obtained? |
| Conclusion | —Summary of the overall results in relation to available literature<br>—Directions/recommendations for future research |
| References | —A listing of all the materials used in a consistent and appropriate style |

tions. It will normally be in this section that the majority of tables, graphs, and figures will appear, and these are expected to be appropriate summaries derived from descriptive or inferential statistics. It is also important not to repeat the same information from tables in the figures. Each table/figure should present their own data set, and it is incumbent on the writer to determine if data may be better presented as a table or as a figure (in the form of a chart or graph—see below for further description). Overall, this section presents a picture of the results of the study, but discussion of those results is left to the next section.

## Discussion

This section is usually the most important part of the paper, and it is here that the consideration of the data and how it relates to the problem or theme takes place. The significance and meaning of the findings presented in the results section are discussed within the context of the methodology of the study and in relation to the previously cited literature. You will find this section easiest to understand if you write it with the same order of ideas/topics that you presented in the Introduction and Results sections. Discussion sections may be extensive, with expanded discussions pointing to the importance of findings shown in the tables and graphs, or may be very short, or even merged into the conclusion section.

One useful rule is that the discussion should not be the largest section of the paper (Hailman and Strier 1997). The overall responsibility of the discussion section is to show that the project fulfilled its objectives, or did not, and to present a considered concise analysis of the results. A discussion will also normally reference the relevant materials in the literature and attempt to reconcile the new findings with the older information. This section is expected to deal with the development toward reaching a conclusion relevant to the research question that was presented in the Introduction.

## Conclusion

This section sometimes stands alone but is also sometimes merged into the discussion section. Writers often have problems with this section. This can be seen in published as well as student reports that range from terse, abbreviated listings of the major conclusions to lengthy discourses that do more to confuse the issues than to enlighten them. It is recommended that conclusion sections—a concise summing up—is the place to present conclusions drawn from the results outlined in the earlier sections. An appropriate length is one page for a term paper or article and 5–10 pages for a graduate thesis, but this can vary significantly. The conclusion should deal with all the questions posed in the introduction. Most critically, it *must* be based on the data collected. The results, followed by the discussion, should lead the reader to already hold the same perceptions as found in the written component. The most important component of the conclusion is a clear answer to the question proposed in the introduction. While caveats regarding the research in the report can be stated, a classic student *faux pas* is to provide a concluding statement that denies all of the work and data presented in preceding sections. The concluding section also sometimes contains directions for future research based on the current work.

# Illustrative Materials

The common illustrative materials employed in scientific reports are tables, photographs, and graphs. Note that photographs and graphs are usually referred to as "figures." Tables and graphs can appear in innumerable styles and forms, but each has the basic features that are common to the class. Tables are summaries of data presented in rows and columns that enable comparisons to be made between categories, and between individual categories and sum totals. The formats for common frequency and duration tables were discussed in chapter 6.

Graphs are typically two-dimensional visual representations of data that could be, and often are, presented in tabular form. There is a certain degree of redundancy between tables and graphs; preference for one or the other depends on perceptual pattern and taste, but tables provide exact data while the graph gives only an approximation. Note, however, that visualizations of data can convey significantly more information in a short period of time to the reader than can a dense table of numbers. Each unit of illustrative material, a table, a graph, or an image, should, indeed must, stand on its own. It should be possible to understand and interpret the data contained within the illustration and its caption without reference to the text body of the document. It is important that the data presented in a graph be easily identified and assimilated; thus, it is important to keep graphic presentations as simple and clean as possible. At the same time, each must be complete. Each table, graph, photograph, or figure needs a title, appropriate labels, and an explanatory caption. Sometimes photographs are the only appropriate mechanism to illustrate a specific situation, condition, or response pattern. The amount of information present in a photograph is much higher than in any graphic, but must be framed, cropped, and captioned to be useful. It is generally inappropriate for a photo-essay to be submitted unless specifically asked for, however, a good photograph is never out of place as an illustrative elaboration. As illustrative material, the following examples of tables, graphs, and photos are presented and their features discussed.

## Tables

Table 7.2 shows the subject animals, a subset of the adult males of the Arashiyama "A" troop residing in south Texas, in a study of their postural behavior. The table is provided with a title, the columns are labeled, each subgroup is identified and provided with a small illustration symbolizing the differences, and the rows are filled in with the appropriate data. This table shows the tattoo number on each subject's face, the common name used by the colony manager, the matriline to which the subject belongs, and his birth year. At the same time,

**Table 7.2  Sample males in a postural study. Males selected for the study were separated into long and short body length categories. Note the differences in birth dates. The troop was moved to Texas in 1972.**

| Males | Tattoo number | Common name | Family | Birth year |
|-------|--------------|-------------|--------|-----------|
| Short-bodied Males | 001 | Fatboy | Rheus | 1971 |
|  | 028 | Suma | Suma | 1964 |
|  | 064 | Moe | Momo | 1964 |
|  | 128 | Hulk | Meme | 1965 |
|  | 134 | Ran68 | Ran | 1968 |
| Long-bodied Males | 002 | Dermot 2 | Pelka | 1970 |
|  | 055 | Wania One Eye | Wania | 1970 |
|  | 074 | Fang | Rotte | 1970 |
|  | 129 | Rocky Two | Betta | 1971 |
|  | 143 | Dermot 1 | Pelka | 1968 |

the table clearly shows the two categories into which this population of males has been divided and gives some indication of the criterion used to do so.

While tables are common mechanisms to present substantial masses of data in an organized format, the information often becomes more useful when presented in the form of a graph, and it has become simple to generate graphs in a multitude of styles, forms, and variants with readily available computer programs. The data analysis program Excel is able to integrate the analysis functions with the capability of generating graphs quickly and easily. However, Excel is limited in the types of graphs it can produce and if you are going so far as to submit your paper for publication, the graphs produced in Excel are usually not produced at a high enough resolution to be published. Statistics programs will produce graphs as well but these vary in their quality. A few programs capable of producing high-quality graphs include Sigma Plot, R, Gephi, Gnuplot, and Matplotlib. It will be profitable to invest a few hours in learning to operate a graphics program.

## Graphs

When creating a graph, it is necessary to bear in mind that a graph requires a title (or caption) below it explaining what is portrayed. The values and scales on axes, legends, and keys must also be defined. A graph, often enclosed within a box on the printed page should be interpretable by itself, without the need to refer to the accompanying text to understand the presentation. Figure 7.1 shows the features expected in a bar graph, and Figure 7.2 presents a graph with several overlain blocks of data. Figure 7.1 shows a title for the graph, labels for the horizontal and vertical axes, and a legend. The values and tick marks on both axes are indicated by the italic comments. Legends are typically only used when more than one set of values is being illustrated in a stacked or grouped bar graph.

It should be noted when using error bars that some styles can give false impressions. Commonly, a mean is graphed and the error bars represent the standard deviation, standard error, or variance. If error bars are employed to show the range around a graphed value but only the upper portion of the error bar is shown (i.e., in what is sometimes called a "pinhead" graph), this gives the impression that the error bars are symmetrical (i.e., the same on the positive and negative side of the mean). Though this may be the case, one must make sure before employing this type of graph. If the upper and lower error bars are not representing equal values, a graph such as this is inappropriate, and instead the upper and lower parts of the error bar should both be shown, as they are in Figure 7.3.

Figure 7.4 presents a distinctive and useful graph, one that represents the differences from the mean (known as the "deviations" and used in chapter 6 for the calculation of standard deviation). This type of graph is based on data derived by subtracting the average value for the species behavior from the

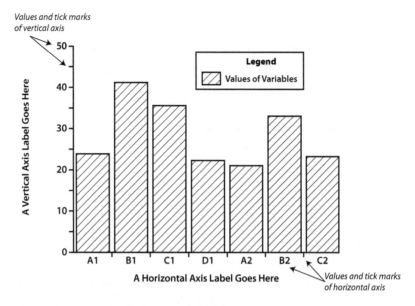

**Figure 7.1**   An example of a bar graph (title).

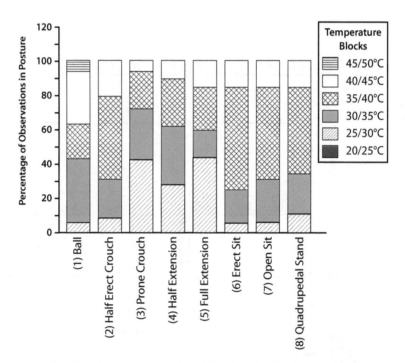

**Figure 7.2**   Graphs of postures employed by short-bodied males in different temperature blocks.

average for all species (at least in Figure 7.4). Values derived will be either positive or negative and when entered into a spreadsheet will produce this type of graph. This form of graph is also valuable for showing differences between individuals or age and sex classes within a group and may be produced in the same way.

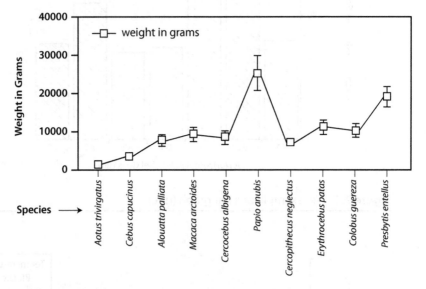

**Figure 7.3** Line graph of primates weights with error bars.

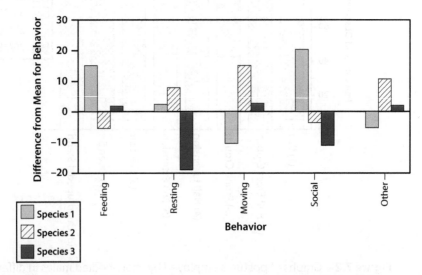

**Figure 7.4** Graph of differences from mean values in time budgets of three species.

## Images

Sometimes an image or set of images is the most useful way to display or help explain your data. Images used within a report are treated similarly to graphs and tables, each must have a title, appropriate labels, and explanatory captions as shown below in Figure 7.5 and Figure 7.6. As should be obvious by now, it is also customary to number tables and graphics (including images) separately and in sequence. Note that if images are not owned by you, they must be cited, and permission must be granted from the previous publisher and creator/photographer if you plan to publish them.

If you are incorporating photographs into your work, it is pertinent that you ensure that they portray the same information in color and grayscale. These will often be printed out in grayscale due to the cost or lack of availability of color printing.

**Figure 7.5** Two samango monkey (*Cercopithecus albogularis*) juveniles play, showing characteristic play faces where the mouth is open with the top teeth covered and the bottom teeth exposed. Steffen Foerster/Shutterstock.

**Figure 7.6**
A subadult male vervet monkey (*Chlorocebus pygerythrus*) participates in a rope-pulling experiment in June 2013 at Lake Nabugao, Uganda. Photos: J. A. Teichroeb.

**Figure 7.6**
*(continued)*

97

# Appendices

Appendices are not normally utilized in a student report, but they occasionally turn up in professional papers and are a common feature of books and monographs. An appendix is used to expand on a particular aspect of the document, and may at times assume the characteristics of an expanded footnote. In other cases, especially where a mathematical proof for an ecological mechanism is needed as supportive evidence, the appropriate location for it is in an appendix.

Appendices are also used to present extensive listings of species located in an environment or to provide a complete ethogram in cases where the data are relevant, but placing it within the text would disrupt the line of thought being presented. In the case of data sharing, which is becoming more common in published works, small data sets may also be included as appendices. The essence of an appendix is that it provides something extra to the reader, but is not necessary to an understanding of the document. It is important when providing appendices that everything is labeled appropriately so that a reader can understand what is being shared without referring to the main text of the document.

# Bibliographic Formats

When writing scientific reports, your instructor will typically lay out the type of bibliographic format you should adhere to. As noted earlier, the most common citation pattern in primatology is that of the APA (Author-Date) style, only adding page numbers for a direct quote, and bibliographic references also follow variations on the standard APA format. The references employed in this chapter are set out below for illustration. Note the pattern: Journal names (e.g., *Behaviour, Primates*) should be set in italics, and book titles are treated the same whether the citation is of a chapter or section within an edited volume or an independent book (i.e., the difference between the DeVore and Washburn [1963], and Oxnard [1983] references). Personal communications are not placed in the bibliography; instructors may, however, wish citations of their class notes or lectures to be included. For more information on APA formatting, you can reference the most current edition of the *Publication Manual of the American Psychological Association* or the APA Style website. However, there is a good deal of variation within this formatting style, and students will find various primate and other related journals will vary in several aspects of formatting, but still be considered general APA style.

# Critical Reading and Reviewing in Primatology

A critical approach to the reading of scientific literature is an important aspect of any research work, and it may be the case that a student will be asked to produce a critical review of a set of research papers as a component of a course. It is important to recognize that this process of critical reading is not simply "turning on the bullsh*t detector," nor is it intended to be a route to trashing or praising the author for style or content alone. Most appropriately, a critical review should be directed at the methods the authors used and their execution as presented in the paper. A series of questions may serve as a guide in this endeavor.

1. What are the research questions posed by the author(s)? Are these clearly presented?

2. What are the formal hypotheses being tested? If they are not visible, how are they implied, or are they to remain a mystery?

3. What variables have been established to evaluate the hypotheses? How are these variables "measured"?

4. Do these variables and their measurements have the logical capability of rejecting the hypothesis? If they do not, is this then a "scientific" inquiry?

5. Has the author incorporated all these aspects into a cohesive whole? Has the author done what was proposed in the research questions? Have the hypotheses been appropriately tested?

6. Only at this point should the reviewer be prepared to turn to issues of style, logic, and grammar in the final product.

Any student in primatology is expected to learn to read critically among the primary literature available. This brings up the point that one should not rely on secondary literature. Secondary literature comes in three forms, which vary in their reliability. Textbooks that synthesize the work of others for general consumption are secondary literature and these can be subject to biases of interpretation. So-called "meta-analyses" where an author reanalyzes or performs a secondary analysis of data collected by others is also secondary literature. Reliance on this form is acceptable but to a limited extent in discussions of secondary sources. Finally, the worst type of source that a student can easily access is websites. Some of these could be considered secondary literature but many are so biased and error-laden that this label is too generous. Students should never rely on websites or use the information in them in their reports.

The best way to utilize secondary literature is to find important primary literature through their citations. If a student relies on secondary sources, they are abdicating responsibility for evaluating and understanding the original work for themselves, leaving it to another individual who may or may not have similar perceptions of it. One of the most consistent error patterns seen in beginning primatology students is an excessive and inappropriate reliance on secondary literature.

**(Smith and Jones 1893 is fictitious, as are rabbitoes, in case you had not guessed.)**

# EIGHT

# Technological Applications for Observational Data Collection

In the last decade, behavioral data collection of primates and other wild animals has changed dramatically. With the rapid expansion in the use of smartphones and tablets, along with an almost unimaginable variety of apps available for these devices, behavioral data collection has moved from pencil and paper to mobile technology. Many field primatologists that were collecting data before the mobile technology onslaught continue with traditional methods; however, embracing these new technologies can make data collection easier, more streamlined, productive, and less prone to error if one follows the GIGO rule.

## Traditional Methods

Using a pencil and paper is a simple and cost-effective way to collect behavioral data in the field. One can either preprint check-sheets or sampling sheets (see chapter 2 for reference) or simply record data on blank sheets of paper or in notebooks. The only supplies required are pencils/pens and paper, so it is inexpensive. There is no need for charging devices or backup batteries, you need not take steps to prevent exposure of high-tech equipment to the elements, and your data are not subject to potential loss from technology breakdowns. Further, data that are accidentally or incorrectly recorded can be easily and quickly changed. Some field primatologists supplement traditional methods by using small portable voice recording devices to record systematic behavioral or *ad libitum* data, either because some subjects move too quickly or are too high in the canopy to reliably record behavior using pencil and paper or mobile devices (e.g., spider monkeys), or to supplement focal or scan data.

However, there are disadvantages associated with data collection using traditional methods. Perhaps most importantly, the task of transposing handwritten or recorded data into manageable data sets for analyses (using spreadsheets like Excel or Access) can be monumental and take significant time. Manually transposing data is also subject to human error, which is not the case with electronic downloads. It also generally takes more time to physically write down the observed behaviors than it would to quickly log them into a mobile device, though this lag time can depend on the program/app being used and how detailed the ethogram is. Additionally, with all of one's data (that may have taken years or more to collect) "living" on paper, the data are subject to loss or destruction. Finally, researchers can display a tendency to be overly descriptive in their observations, building up a large volume of "unique" details that cannot be readily analyzed by statistical procedures.

# Mobile Technologies

We use the term "mobile technologies" to include smartphones and tablets as devices using mobile applications and/or downloadable software programs to collect data. The use of mobile technologies to collect behavioral data provides several important benefits to the researcher. First, one can quickly download data from a mobile device directly into a spreadsheet for data organization and analyses, enabling a much more efficient and less error-prone means of transposing data. Second, the lag time is generally reduced from the time the behavior is observed to the time it is actually recorded, which translates to increased accuracy of data (provided that the correct behaviors were input!). Third, with the advent of cloud data storage, once data are backed up they cannot (theoretically) be lost. Finally, using mobile technologies generally restricts the format and type of data collected by the observer, intensely focusing attention on clear behaviors as they have been input into an ethogram.

However, using mobile technologies to collect data can be costly (the mobile device, backup batteries, cloud/external device storage costs, software, protective device cases, and so on), and researchers must be much more vigilant about protecting valuable devices from rain, wind, dust, and other hazards that fieldwork can subject them to. Working in remote areas may also prevent access to electricity and/or the internet, so downloading data to the cloud may have to be substituted by downloading to an external storage device. Finally, because using mobile technologies restricts you to your sample data collection as input into your ethogram (which is desirable as discussed above), it can also be more difficult to record and describe *ad libitum* data for rare events. For example, Julie Teichroeb observed infanticide events during her fieldwork, which required extensive qualitative descriptions of multiple actors that would have been difficult to enter into a mobile device. One way around this is to always have a dictating machine or a field notebook with you when you are collecting data so that you can record observations of rare behaviors in detail if you see them. Some mobile applications and downloadable programs can also be programmed to allow for additional, less structured data to be recorded.

In considering the use of a mobile device for observational recording, the following five points should be considered (adapted from Lehner 1996).

1. Is the device able to do the job? Does it have sufficient memory to hold the expected amount of data that will be collected? Does the software/ app have sufficient customizability to ensure the most detailed data are collected as required for the research question/s?

2. Is the device appropriately portable? Can the observer easily hold the device and collect data while following animals? Will the process of data entry interfere excessively with the maintenance of observation? Will the weight of the device cause excessive fatigue in the observer?

3. How is the device powered and repaired? Is a power source available if recharging is necessary? Is it readily serviceable or replaceable? Is service/replacement available near the research location? Is the manufacturer able and/or willing to provide quick mail or courier repair service at a reasonable cost? Is the price such that a spare can be taken to the field?

4. What do you do if your device becomes inoperative and nonreplaceable? Is there a backup research design and/or data collecting procedure?

In the end, the selection and implementation of mobile technologies are based on personal evaluation and preference as well as research questions and cost. It is wise to remember Murphy's Law, "If anything can go wrong, it will." Plan for it, expect it, and be prepared to revise plans as necessary.

## Mobile Applications/Software Programs

The information presented here represents options for collecting behavioral data in a field, laboratory, or zoo setting using mobile technologies (Table 8.1). The organization and analyses of collected data are presented elsewhere (chapters 6 and 9), but generally this would be undertaken using software programs such as Excel, Access, R, SPSS, and others. Note that mobile applications and software programs that can be downloaded for data collection are constantly changing, but at the time of publication these are some of the most commonly used programs by primatologists. Some are apps or programs designed specifically for primate or other animal data collection, and some are general software platforms used for mobile forms design that would be downloadable onto a mobile device. All are customizable to some point.

The apps and software programs specifically designed for primate or other animal data collection generally provide options for focal animal and scan sampling, and some also include other forms of sample collection such as one/zero or focal time sampling. Some are much more sophisticated and allow the observer to "nest" data, such that several important behaviors can be collected simultaneously (e.g., an individual is feeding on a specific species and plant part, and is doing so nearby three other individuals, so feeding and social data can be collected). Others are not as sophisticated and may only allow basic ethograms to be input. Some have easy learning curves and others take more time to learn and set up; some are open-source (free) and others have either small or significant costs associated with acquiring them.

The list here is by no means complete, particularly if you are considering using a mobile forms design software platform as there are many more options than those listed here. Many factors contribute to choosing an appropriate program. Researchers must consider what form of data collection is right for them, whether the interface is easy to use, what their research questions are (i.e., is the program customizable so that all the required data can be easily collected and analyzed?), what the field conditions are, and the availability of equipment and funds. Finally, students should be aware that when animals move quickly

**Table 8.1 Available mobile applications and software programs useful for behavioral/ecological data collection in primate studies.**

| Application Name | Platform | Open-source? | Availability |
|---|---|---|---|
| CyberTracker | Windows PC, then download app to any mobile device | Yes | https://www.cybertracker.org/ |
| Animal Observer | Customizable with R, download app to iPhone or iPad only | Yes | http://fosseyfund.github.io/AOToolBox/ |
| Animal Behavior Pro | Download app from app store directly to mobile iOS device only | Yes | https://research.kent.ac.uk/lprg/software/ & https://apps.apple.com/us/app/animal-behaviour-pro/id579588319 |
| Prim8 Software | Download to PC and then to Android mobile device, or directly to Android mobile device from the website | Yes | http://www.prim8software.com/ |
| JWatcher | Download Java-based software on PC or Mac only | Yes | http://www.jwatcher.ucla.edu/ |
| ZooMonitor | Web-based app designed for use with Android, Windows, or iOS tablets | No | https://zoomonitor.org/home |
| Obansys | Download from app store directly to mobile iOS device only | Free and paid versions available | https://www.mangold-international.com/en/products/software/mobile-observation-with-obansys |
| Noldus The Observer | Pocket Observer downloadable from Windows PC to Android mobile device | No | https://www.noldus.com/ |
| BORIS (Behavioral Observation Research Interactive Software) | Downloadable on Windows, Mac, or Linux systems, or as an app for Android mobile device | Yes | http://www.boris.unito.it/ |
| Solomon Coder | Downloadable on Windows PC only | Yes | https://solomoncoder.com/ |
| Neukadye "Time Stamped Fieldnotes" | Download from app store directly on iOS mobile devices only | No (but cost is nominal) | https://www.neukadye.com/ |
| BehaviorCloud | Download to iOS or Android devices; focus on video data | No | https://behaviorcloud.com/academia.html |
| Pendragon Forms | Windows PC, then download app to any iOS or Android mobile device | No | https://www.pendragonforms.com/ |
| Fulcrum | Download to iOS, Android, desktop, or from web; more applicable to survey data | No | https://www.fulcrumapp.com/ |
| Excel | Can use tablets with customized Excel macros | Yes (if you have the expertise and program available) | |

*An often updated version of this list is also on the website.

or are high in the canopy, it may be challenging to enter accurate data onto a mobile device (or using pencil and paper) and keep your eyes on the animal at the same time. With practice your ability to do this will improve, but in these circumstances a team of two (i.e., an animal spotter and a data recorder) is often employed. Only with a voice recorder can the observer's attention be simultaneously on the animal and the data collection device.

Exercises appropriate to any of the listed mobile technologies would be a repeat of the focal time sampling (exercise 8) or focal animal sampling (exercise 9) exercises. The utilization of a mobile device for data collection in no way changes the characteristics and protocols of either form of study. Conduct of these exercises using mobile technologies is considered to be advanced-level work since it is reliant on access to computer equipment.

# NINE

# Software and Methods of Data Storage, Compilation, and Analyses

$E$ven the smallest study on primate behavior will result in many pages or columns of data that need to be analyzed. These can potentially be tallied and analyzed by hand but there is no need to attempt this given the wide range of time-saving tools available to help. Researchers have different techniques for dealing with their data and these are often specific to the subfield of primatology that they are working in and the types of data they collect. In this chapter, we will discuss various methods and the software that can be used to tally, compile, store, and analyze data. However, if you are working on something unusual, what may be best for your particular data sets may be something that we have not covered.

## Spreadsheets vs. Databases

The first thing that is typically done after, or while, collecting data is to organize it into rows and columns of information in some kind of software. While this may seem simple, there are some important considerations at this stage, the first of which is what software to use. A fundamental concept here is the difference between spreadsheet programs and databases. These look similar on the surface but differ in several important ways. Both types of technologies are used to store and manage data sets but they vary in how they do this.

**Spreadsheets**—store data values in cells and allow cells to refer to or process values based on other cells.

The most popular spreadsheet program is Microsoft Excel but others are available including those through OpenOffice and the Google Suite. Spreadsheets are designed to organize, sort, and analyze lists of data. They allow you to crunch numbers and perform calculations and basic descriptive statistics, though for more complicated statistics you will need to use a statistical program (see below). Since data can be so easily manipulated and sorted in a spreadsheet, mistakes can easily occur where cells that should be associated become disassociated. If two or more people are using a data set, the data integrity over the long term will be greatly increased if a database is used rather than a spreadsheet.

**Databases**—store values in tables that are individually named. Each row in the table is called a "record" and databases are made to link tables and associate the records in each.

Two of the most commonly used databases are Microsoft Access and Oracle, but there are many more. The primary function of databases is for the long-term storage of large amounts of raw data. Since data are not manipulated at the cell level in a database, data integrity is maintained even if many users have access.

We recommend that for beginning students of primate behavior spreadsheets are used since they are easy to learn and do not require the higher level of technological expertise that is required for databases. Tabulation and calculations can also be easily accomplished. However, students should be aware of how spreadsheets work and how they can affect data integrity if one is not careful.

## Data Organization

The next consideration before entering your data is how it will be organized in the program you choose. For ease of entering data, there is often a temptation to just put it into a spreadsheet in the way that it was collected. In some cases, this method will work fine, as is often the case with scan sample data. However, it is important to think about what you eventually want to pull out of the data, and how you are going to analyze it before you begin entering it. This is especially the case if you are not using a data collection device and are not automatically locked into one format for your data input.

For focal animal sampling, for instance, it may be beneficial to do some tallying and reorganization of the data as it is entered. As an example, we can use a 10-minute focal animal sample collected by one of the authors (Teichroeb) on an ursine (or white-thighed) colobus monkey (*Colobus vellerosus*) in Ghana. Table 9.1 shows the data as they were collected as time-stamped changes in behavior recorded first on a dictaphone and then transcribed to paper. However, since this field research had multiple goals, these data were entered differently into a spreadsheet with some initial tallying done on entry. The first goal of these samples was determining the patterns of diet, associated food competition, and their effects on social behavior. However, patterns of vigilance were also recorded during focal samples to maximize data collection. Table 9.2 shows how the same focal animal sample was entered to make later analyses easier.

## Data Analyses With Spreadsheet Programs

Spreadsheet programs allow you to easily calculate all the descriptive statistics that are listed in chapter 6. The *Formulas* tab in Excel, for instance, has many common mathematical functions already loaded. If the formula you need is not there, you can also easily make your own formula to apply to, and relate, various cells. Two features of spreadsheet programs that are particularly useful for initial assessments of your data are the filtering and sorting function and the ability to build pivot tables.

**Table 9.1   Focal animal sample on a white-thighed colobus monkey.**

Date: July 24, 2005
Group/observer: B2/JT
Time: 11:10
Quadrat/tree: 186SF
Height: 10 m
Individual: AF – Grace

| Time | Behavior State | Event |
|------|---------------|-------|
| 0:00 | Rest | |
| 0:09 | | Juv approach to 1m, scan |
| 0:12 | | scratch |
| 0:20 | Auto-grm | |
| 0:39 | g grm Juv | scan |
| 2:07 | Rest | |
| 2:09 | g grm Juv | |
| 2:55 | Rest | scan |
| 3:27 | | scan |
| 3:33 | | scratch, scan |
| 3:39 | | scan |
| 3:47 | g grm Juv | r grm pres Juv |
| 3:52 | Rest | |
| 4:00 | g grm Juv | scan |
| 4:15 | r grm pres Juv | |
| 5:05 | | scan |
| 5:24 | Rest | r grm pres Juv, scan |
| 5:35 | | scratch |
| 5:46 | | scan |
| 6:09 | | scan |
| 7:11 | | scan |
| 8:16 | | scan |
| 9:27 | | scan |

- **Filter and sorting functions:** By applying the *Filter* function, you can pull out subsets of your data. For instance, you can filter out all the data for each age-sex class to allow comparisons, or find all the rows of data for a particular individual, and so on. If you apply filters to multiple columns at a time, you can narrow down your data. For example, by sorting three columns you could pull out all the "adult females" that "groomed" in the "low canopy." The *Sort* function allows you to put data in order easily, which can be useful when building histograms and other graphs. You can also customize the filter function so that you can pull out certain bins of values or particular data records.

- **Pivot tables:** These are excellent for exploring large data sets in a quicker, easier format than filtering and sorting. They also allow you to make links between different types of data and sum all the records for various

**Table 9.2    Entry of the focal animal sample from Table 9.1 into a spreadsheet.**

| Date* | Time | Group | Age-Sex | ID | Duration(s) | Height (m) | Feeding occurred?† | Grooming occurred? | Groom bout duration(s) | Grooming direction | Grooming bout truncated?†‡ | # Grooming bouts in the sample | Other social behavior duration(s) | Auto-grooming duration(s) | Approaches given | Approaches received | Other social events | Scans |
|---|---|---|---|---|---|---|---|---|---|---|---|---|---|---|---|---|---|---|
| 7/24/05 | 11:10 | B2 | AF | GR | 600 | 10 | N | Y | 88 | g grm juv | N | 4 | | 19 | | Juv | 3 r grm pres juv | 14 |
| 7/24/05 | 11:10 | B2 | AF | GR | | | | | 46 | g grm juv | N | | | | | | | |
| 7/24/05 | 11:10 | B2 | AF | GR | | | | | 5 | g grm juv | N | | | | | | | |
| 7/24/05 | 11:10 | B2 | AF | GR | | | | | 84 | g grm juv | N | | | | | | | |

* Data in the first five columns are carried down to all rows to facilitate sorting in the spreadsheet program later. This allows you to make sure that you can sort out all the rows that belong to a particular sample.

† If feeding had occurred in this focal animal sample and a Y was here to indicate yes, another set of columns and rows would be added that would allow the duration of each feeding bout to be included, as well as what species and food item were consumed during each bout.

‡ This indicates whether or not the grooming bout was truncated. Grooming that occurs at the beginning or the end of the focal animal sample would be truncated (i.e., the duration recorded is not the total duration of the grooming bout). It is important to know this information about any state behavior bout duration for consideration in later statistical analyses.

categories of data. In Excel, if you go to the *Insert* tab and look in the upper left corner, it will even provide you with a list of suggested pivot tables. Once you click on one, a menu on the side will allow you to add and remove fields in your pivot table with a click.

Despite the usefulness of spreadsheets, if you wish to go beyond basic descriptive statistics and use more complicated inferential statistics you will likely have to use a statistical program. We discuss these below.

## Statistical Programs

There are many statistical programs available and the basic data entry into these is usually in the format of a spreadsheet, which makes it easy to copy and paste rows and columns from a spreadsheet or database program. Some commonly used statistical programs include SPSS/PASW, SAS, SYSTAT, Prism by Graphpad, among others (see Table 4.3 for a list of some commonly used statistical software programs). Many of these have high subscription fees that can be prohibitive for students. For relatively simple statistics, there are often free online calculators that can be used. Currently, one of the best websites for explaining the theory behind the tests and providing calculators is www.vassarstats.net.

If you are a student that wants to continue into any science, we strongly recommend that you take a basic seminar or course on how to use R (The R Project for Statistical Computing). The learning curve is high in R because you have to use programming language; however, since R is an open-source program (i.e., free) and powerful (i.e., it can do almost anything needed for primatology data analysis), R is the most widely used statistical program in the sciences. For ease of use, we recommend first downloading R Studio (www.rstudio.com) in addition to the R program (www.r-project.org). R Studio offers a user-friendly interface for R and makes it easier to upload your data, see what R packages you are using, and access help pages on them. There are many online help sources for any analyses that you wish to carry out in R.

Finally, we will end this chapter with an important truism. While the information on software and applications in this and the previous chapter is current at the time of writing, technology moves at a breakneck pace. It is the responsibility of students to investigate new and useful tools as they become available.

# TEN

# Field Gear, Equipment, and Accessories

$A$ny fieldwork project requires budgeting for equipment, observational tools, clothing, vaccinations, antimalarial and other drugs, and a multitude of gear needed to survive and work in a bush or forest environment. While this workbook is not intended to cover the necessities for fieldwork in detail, it is appropriate to make some recommendations that may help to avoid problems.

First, some books that will be of value to planning a field project:

- Doyle, G. S. 2010. *Where there is no doctor: Preventive and emergency healthcare in uncertain times*. Process Self-Reliance Series.

- Krebs, C. J. 1999. *Ecological methodology*, 2nd ed. Addison-Wesley Educational Publishers: Menlo Park, CA.

- Lehner, P. 1996. *Handbook of ethological methods*, 2nd ed. Cambridge University Press: Cambridge.

- Martin, P., and Bateson, P. 2007. *Measuring behaviour: An introductory guide*, 3rd ed. Cambridge University Press: Cambridge.

- Rees, P. A. 2015. *Studying captive animals: A workbook of methods in behaviour, welfare and ecology*. John Wiley & Sons: West Sussex, U.K.

- Setchell, J. M., and Curtis, D. J. (Eds.). 2011. *Field and laboratory methods in primatology: A practical guide*, 2nd ed. Cambridge University Press: Cambridge.

- Wiseman, J. 2014. *The SAS survival handbook: The ultimate guide to surviving anywhere*, 3rd ed. Harper Collins: London.

The first volumes in this listing are two of the most concise and practical collections of medical and survival information currently available. While much of what they contain is not specific to primatology studies, the material can be of great value and serves as a solid practical introduction to some of the problems that can be encountered in field conditions. Many will reject Wiseman (2014) merely because of its military ancestry, but the field experiences are directly applicable to the circumstances of a primate observer. Look for the practicalities and keep an open mind. The other five volumes supplement and complement this workbook. They provide in-depth coverage of many aspects that are not treated here, as well as providing methodological tools to expand the research plan.

Countless online sources help field biologists and primatologists in gathering required equipment, supplies, and other gear necessary for successful field research, all one has to do is a simple online search. The number of products that can be found online is dizzying, so this chapter is meant to provide some guidance on what is often necessary and most helpful. There are some basic supplies and equipment that almost all field primatologists use, and some supplementary gear that may be useful depending on the:

- research questions addressed,

- study species,

- duration of the research,

- geography and political climate of the area where research will be undertaken,

- degree of remoteness of the field site,

- availability of supplies in the area, and

- budget.

Note that the choice of field gear can also be highly personal in terms of the types of supplies, equipment, clothing that are preferred, and the available budget. The following provides a listing of different types of gear one can expect to include on their research project, though it is not considered exhaustive. Check with experienced fieldworkers or mentors for a list of appropriate gear for your project and geographic area.

## Basic Field Supplies and Equipment

Ensure that you are familiar with the most updated regulations in the country where you will be conducting your field research. Some countries prevent the importation of certain items that may seem necessary to those of us in industrialized nations; for example, many African nations now prohibit the importation of plastic bags. It is a good idea to consult the government website for the country in question to answer any common questions you may have before departure. The following provides a basic list of essentials to consider:

- **Laptop computer.** Used for downloading data, analyses, and so on.

- **Binoculars.** See below for guidance.

- **Handheld GPS.** Used for basic navigation, and to mark important locations that contribute to your research (e.g., primate groups/individuals, home ranges, day ranges, trees). See below for more guidance.

- **Mobile device.** If you are using one to collect data.

- **Stopwatch/watch.** Useful for primate follows if you are not using a mobile device. May also be useful as your alarm clock in the morning.

- **Small voice recorder.** Useful for accurately dictating rare behaviors without taking your eyes off your study subjects.

- **Notebooks.** Even if you are using a mobile device, it is important to have a notebook for field log data. "Rite-in-the-Rain" notebooks are best as the paper is treated to resist water, but they are more expensive.

- **Pencils/pens/sharpies**. Sharpies are permanent and useful for writing on everything from bags to vials (if you are collecting biological samples), and everything in between.
- **Calculator**. Useful if you do not have a mobile device or require a calculator with more functions for data analysis.
- **Flagging tape**. Used for marking trees, trails, and field equipment (if they are dropped in the forest flagging tape makes them easier to see and recover).
- **Pocket knife/Leatherman**. Handy and useful for just about anything.
- **Flashlight/headlamp/batteries**. Particularly useful if your electricity is limited or unavailable at your field site, but helpful otherwise. Headlamps are highly recommended for reading and working at night because your hands are free.
- **Clipboard**. Useful for recording data if you are not using a mobile device.
- **Water bottles/hydration pack**. It is imperative to stay hydrated all day! We tell our students to carry at least 3 liters of water into the field daily. Nalgene or the aluminum bottles with simple caps (fancy ones tend to get caught on twigs and branches in the forest) work well.
- **Flash drive**. Useful for moving and backing up data regularly. Given that these can fill up or stop working, two or more may be necessary.
- **Day pack/lumbar pack**. The style for this item is a personal preference, but at a minimum get one that is lightweight and big enough to carry all your daily field supplies.
- **UV blocking sunglasses**. Useful to protect your eyes in and out of forested sites.
- **Lightweight packable towel/s**. Depending on where you stay, these can be indispensable. They also dry quickly so they won't start to smell in humid climates.
- **Laundry bag**. If you are lucky enough to have a place to take your laundry, fabric laundry bags are more durable and environmentally friendly than plastic garbage bags.
- **Carabiners**. You can never have too many to attach gear to your pack.
- **Large rubber bands**. Useful for rolling up your poncho when it's wet, keeping supplies together in your pack, and all sorts of other handy uses.
- **Camera and lenses**. See below for guidance.
- **Extra chargers/batteries for all electronics**. Sets of rechargeable batteries and backup battery packs are essential the more you rely on electronics to collect and organize your data.
- **Duct tape**. Useful for anything!

- **Ziploc bags**. While we encourage students to reduce their use of plastic bags, they can be useful for keeping gear (and lots of other things) separated, dry, and protected.

- **Waterproof protection for mobile devices**. Rather than relying on plastic bags to protect your valuable mobile devices, we recommend using cases made specifically for protection from water, dust, and unexpected drops.

- **First aid and snake bite kits**. A small, portable first aid kit with basic topicals and bandages is essential in the field. A snake bite kit can be a lifesaver if your research is in areas with a high prevalence of venomous snakes. Ensure that you are familiar with how to use a snake bite kit before embarking on your fieldwork.

## Binoculars

A good pair of binoculars is almost an identifying trademark of the experienced field primatologist, and is essential to any successful field project. Since so much time is spent with these devices in front of one's eyes, it is appropriate and wise to obtain the best that you can afford. Topline instruments come from Leica, Zeiss, and Swarovski, and the prices are reflective, ranging from $1,000–$2,000 USD or more. Other manufacturers like Nikon, Vortex, Leupold, and Bushnell produce several distinct grades of quality. A good quality pair of binoculars for fieldwork should be extremely rugged in construction (i.e., waterproof and with a rubberized coating around the housing), have quality glass lenses with good grade multicoating to reduce reflections and ghost images, and come equipped with fold down and adjustable eyecups that allow for use with and without prescription glasses. While many beginning observers elect to use bargain basement or "department store" binoculars, the experiences and clarity of vision are disappointing. When able, field workers should purchase high-quality equipment.

When shopping for binoculars, two numbers are important: the magnification and the objective size, described as 8x40, or 10x42, or others. The first number is the power, or magnification (e.g., 6, 7, 8, or 10 times magnification). Higher magnification brings the subjects closer and is usually more costly; however, when magnification exceeds 10x the image can be more unstable due to user "shake." The second number is the diameter of the objective lenses in millimeters, which indicates how much light can enter the field of view. The larger the number, the more light the lens brings in. If you are working in a forest with a full canopy that does not let in much light, a larger objective lens (e.g., 50) might be worth the larger size, weight, and cost that usually comes with it. In most cases, we recommend 8–10 magnification and a 40–42 objective size as a good general place to start for primate viewing.

Binoculars are generally classified as either "roof" or "porro" prism (Figure 10.1). Roof-prisms are slender and more compact due to the eyepieces and objective lenses being connected in a straight line. They also tend to be more

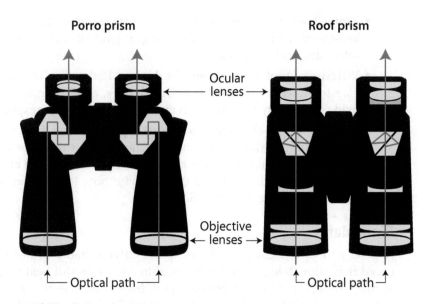

**Figure 10.1** General design of porro vs. roof prism binoculars. Modified from binocularsguides.com.

rugged and expensive than the wider porro-prism designs, though the quality of view is similar or even lower than porro-prisms of equal quality. We recommend roof-prism due to its more streamlined design and ease of use.

Other considerations are field of view (usually the wider the better) and eye relief, which measures the distance between the eyepiece and your eye. The latter is usually described in mm (e.g., from 8 to 24 or more), and the larger the number, generally the more comfortable the viewing, particularly for those that wear eyeglasses. Smaller, more compact binoculars can be convenient due to their lightweight and small size, but the field of view is much lower and the image is typically lower quality.

All the best-quality binoculars will have these features optimized for the normal range of human eyes, and like most things, you get what you pay for. It is important to try different types of binoculars to find those that are most comfortable for you to use and carry. Binocular manufacturers maintain websites with details and data on their products, and the internet can provide a wealth of information on the technical features, advantages, and limitations of the various binocular designs. It is tempting to buy something less expensive, but buying a high-quality pair of binoculars is worth the cost in the end because they will last much longer. Julie Teichroeb agonized about buying a $500 pair of Nikon roof-prism, waterproof, 10x40 binoculars for her master's project in 1999 and she abused them terribly over many years of fieldwork, but they still work great. Lisa Corewyn purchased a similar pair of Nikon Monarch binoculars (excellent quality for the price) that she used for 10 years, sent them to Nikon to repair the eyecups, and they sent her a brand new pair. So, the better brands with long or lifetime warranties can be worth it if you are planning to continue fieldwork.

## Cameras and Lenses

Photography of both faunal and floral wildlife is often a significant part of fieldwork for professional and personal reasons. Professionally, photographs and videos can (1) record identities of individual animals for easier and more reliable reference; (2) record movements and postures related to your ethogram; (3) capture unique or rare behaviors or events; and (4) provide footage for future use in educational and/or scientific presentations (Rees 2015). Personally, photography can provide a fulfilling record of your unique experiences. The purpose of this section is not to lay out a full review of how to achieve competent photography (the details of this process can be found in innumerable photographic manuals and courses), but rather to provide the reader with some basic and practical information to get started.

There are factors to consider before investing in camera/video equipment, and the market is constantly changing and expanding, so choices can be overwhelming. This is complicated by the fact that most of us have a good-quality camera on our smartphones. So, what to do? Digital cameras come in three basic designs, almost all of which also provide video filming options: point-and-shoot, DSLR (digital single-lens reflex), and mirrorless models.

Basic point-and-shoot cameras have fallen out of favor as smartphone cameras have improved, but higher-end models with long zoom lenses, manual controls, and larger sensors are growing in popularity. The advantages of these cameras are their smaller size and weight, sometimes lower cost, and ease of use in not having to carry around several lenses and accompanying gear. The disadvantage largely comes in reduced image quality; however, many of the "superzoom" cameras have increased the size of the sensor so they have improved dramatically, and some argue they can obtain equal or better quality from their superzoom than from a traditional DSLR. The one constant with point-and-shoot models, no matter how sophisticated, is the lack of an interchangeable lens, so they are limited in whatever zoom capabilities are built into the camera (e.g., 30x optical zoom, 50x optical zoom, or others). It cannot be upgraded or swapped out for a different type of lens later.

DSLRs are the workhorse choice for any fieldworker, and run the gamut from consumer to professional models. The advantages of DLSRs are their flexibility and image quality. Many models come with consumer packages that include the camera body, a basic 50–55 mm focal length lens, and a second telephoto or zoom lens. You can invest in better quality, and/or specialty lenses such as fish-eye, wide-angle, telephoto, and macro. For most field primatologists, having a telephoto lens is essential to capturing decent quality photos of primates, particularly if the study species are arboreal and smaller in size. Even an entry-level model DSLR will usually provide better image quality than most point-and-shoot models, though image quality with DLSRs is also a reflection of the expertise of the user. The biggest disadvantage of using a DSLR is the bulk and weight of carrying the camera body and whatever lenses you plan to use. The costs can increase substantially as well, depending on the lens.

Mirrorless cameras provide excellent image quality, the option of interchangeable lenses, and less weight and bulk compared to traditional DSLRs. These cameras do not have a mirror (unlike DSLRs) and they do not have an optical viewfinder, so viewing is only available on the LCD screen. Mirrorless cameras are a good choice if you are planning to take a lot of video due to their on-chip focus sensors, and they are more widely available in high definition and 4K than DSLRs. Prices for mirrorless cameras are usually higher than basic point-and-shoot cameras and go up substantially with the size of the sensor. Other disadvantages include fewer lens choices, and the lack of an optical viewfinder is undesirable for many photographers.

Tropical fieldwork conditions place substantial strains on any camera equipment, though some are made particularly for rugged conditions and the industry has improved substantially in this regard. For example, the advent of sport/action video cameras (e.g., GoPro cameras) has revolutionized our ability to capture footage while we are engaged in the activity itself, and the video quality can be excellent. These types of cameras are also used for field research as video camera traps to capture film of otherwise elusive animals, and/or to monitor populations.

## Global Positioning System (GPS)

Global Positioning System receivers have become an indispensable tool for primatology field projects. The system uses several operational satellites that are orbiting the earth to send information to units on the ground. The primary purpose of GPS for field research is mapping and recording ranging behavior. Increasingly, studies use GPS for multiple purposes, including spatial analyses for group dispersal and dynamics, as well as for ecological analyses.

There are many types of GPS units available, from highly precise and expensive Trimble units to good-quality Garmin or Magellan handhelds. Most handhelds, for example, can obtain a satellite signal very well outside a forest canopy and then "hang on" to the signal for as long as needed once inside the forest, and the accuracy will be within one to 10 meters in nearly all areas of the world. Most smartphones also have GPS capabilities, though the ability to obtain waypoints and tracking information are limited or lacking. GPS receivers are also used as collars (or implants in some instances) for individual animal tracking by incorporating a small receiver into a collar and placing it on the animal so that researchers can follow individual animal movements (see Kays et al. 2015 for more information on using GPS to track animal movements).

# Clothing/Personal Items

What to wear for fieldwork? While this is a personal decision, there are some important considerations. In many countries, it is not appropriate to wear camouflage-patterned clothing under any circumstances as this can lead to a researcher being mistaken for an insurgent or guerrilla. It is safest to avoid military-style clothing even though it may be perfectly suited to the conditions. Some research sites even specify the type and color of clothing that workers are required to wear, but a good practice is to keep to neutral browns, blues, or greens and avoid loud colors or prints as they can be disturbing to wildlife.

One priority for all fieldworkers is to take care of your feet. They are your most important asset and how all work and travel become possible. Fieldworkers commonly acquire broken toes, wrenched/sprained ankles, and even "trench foot" in the field. Good quality, sturdy hiking boots may be the best field equipment that you can spend money on, but they can deteriorate rapidly in the humidity of the tropics. To prevent biting ants, we suggest that pant legs be tucked into socks to keep them from climbing up inside the clothing, and you can use duct tape to seal pant legs to your boots to prevent leeches from crawling inside your socks and boots if you are working in an area where leeches would be an issue.

Here are some suggestions for clothing and footwear:

- **Poncho or lightweight rain jacket**. We encourage students to bring ponchos rather than rain jackets (though both, if possible, would be best) since they are better at covering you and your backpack when it rains. And when it rains in the tropics, it really rains. Do not buy cheap ponchos though, as these will rip in the field the first day and be useless.

- **Field hat or cap**. This is a personal preference in the field if you are working in a shady forest, but essential when out in the sun.

- **Quick-dry field pants**. These are the only way to go when working in the field as you are unlikely to have the luxury of a clothes dryer. We advise students not to invest heavily in clothing, however, as they get dirty, sweaty, and often ripped when working in the field. Used clothing stores are an ideal place to find field clothes.

- **Field shirts**. Again, these are a personal preference, but we recommend some moisture-wicking lightweight T-shirts, and some long sleeve shirts (either moisture-wicking and/or quick-dry) for sun protection and/or if the field site has a lot of biting insects.

- **Moisture-wicking hiking socks**. Get the best quality and quantity that you can afford. Some prefer wool hiking socks and some not, but when you are on your feet all day and sweating, good quality socks are essential. You also want to bring enough to have clean, dry socks each day. There is no worse way to start your field day than by having to put on wet, dirty socks in the morning.

- **Waterproof, durable hiking boots**. Ensure they are durable enough but lightweight as well. Comfort is key, so try to find boots that feel good right out of the box, or use them for a sufficient "break-in" period prior to your trip.

- **Rubber boots**. If you are working in an area during the wet season, or if it is a flooded or muddy area, comfortable rubber boots are a must.

- **Water/hiking sandals**. Not for the field, but essential for time away from the field.

- **Money belt**. Useful for hiding money, passport, and credit cards away from pickpockets in crowded areas like markets.

- **Toiletries**. Depending on what is available to purchase nearby your field site or if you can get to a market, you will need to bring required toiletries such as soap, shampoo, toothpaste, and others. Note that if you wear contact lenses, the solution needed may be impossible to find where you do fieldwork and you will need to bring a supply with you.

- **Over-the-counter medicine**. Again, what you bring depends on local availability, but ensure you have some basics with you for the inevitable upsets that arise, including antidiarrheal tablets, Pepto-Bismol or similar, pain relievers, allergy medication, anti-itch topicals such as cortisone cream, antibiotic cream or iodine, bandages, antifungal cream, and so on.

- **Prescription medication**. While in many countries there are far fewer restrictions for obtaining medications that usually require prescriptions in the U.S. and Canada, you do not want to rely on having to purchase any required medications in-country as they may not be readily available. Bring everything that you need ahead of time to ensure you are covered. We also recommend having a full supply of all the antimalarial pills that you may need for the duration of the trip and a full-spectrum antibiotic with you, in case you become ill. Storing these items in your carry-on baggage during your flight is also a good idea, as lost luggage may be missing for many days and you do not want to be without your medication that long.

- **Insect repellent**. You should always have some with you when you are working in the field, particularly if you will be in a forest where there are almost always mosquitoes or other biting insects. In some cases, you can purchase insect repellent in-country, but in others you cannot, so check with individuals who have worked in the area before departure so you know how much you need to bring with you.

- **Sunscreen**. It is not recommended to go without sunscreen, even if you are working in a shaded forest. Harmful rays can penetrate the forest canopy and do substantial damage over the long term; therefore, we recommend using sunscreen whenever you are in the field and using mineral-based (reef safe) sunscreens where possible.

- **Bandanas**. These are handy to tie your hair, make a sweatband, mop sweat, wave away bugs, wipe away dirt, or use as a fan to keep you cool. Indispensable.

Here are some suggestions for supplemental and optional gear:

- **Portable tent/sleeping pad/pillow.** If you have no accommodations, then you must camp.
- **Sleeping bag**. If you need to camp, or when accommodations are less than ideal.
- **Mosquito net**. Essential if you are in an area of high malaria prevalence. Ensure that you have a fine net so that small no-see-ums cannot get through, and that the mosquito net is treated with permethrin.
- **Snake gaiters/leggings**. If venomous snakes are particularly prevalent in the area where you are undertaking your fieldwork.
- **Water treatment**. If required, bring a water filter, tablets, drops, or steri-pen.
- **Dry bag/stuff sack**. To keep your clothes and other gear dry, particularly in the wet season or in high humidity. Additional packets of silica gel are also useful to keep gear dry.
- **Fleece jacket**. If you are in an area that gets cool at night or during a particular season.
- **Clothesline**. If you are washing or rinsing your clothes as you wear them.
- **Portable solar panels/chargers**. Used to help power small electronics if electricity is unavailable. See below for more guidance.
- **General camping gear for food preparation.** Again, if you have to camp.

## Solar Chargers

Solar charging systems have been the savior of many field stations and research projects in remote field locations where electricity is not available. The systems work by employing a solar panel to collect energy from sunlight and store it in a battery bank using an intelligent charge controller. Designs of these systems vary and have come a long way since their initial introduction to the market a couple of decades ago. They are also reasonably affordable and, depending on the system used, can range in their ability to power small electronics for short periods to being able to power much larger and more substantial pieces of equipment. It also should be recognized that the power available depends on the intensity of sunlight. Cloudy days or shaded installations mean less power, less recharging of batteries, and more circumspect power usage during the evening.

# Ecological Equipment

A multitude of useful and specialized equipment could be listed under the heading of ecological equipment, though whether to include any of those suggested here would depend on your research questions, budget, and the levels of precision required for particular measures.

## Compass

If you are navigating using traditional approaches (and not using your smartphone or handheld GPS), a good-quality compass is a necessity, and there are many available. We recommend the Brunton Pocket Transit, which is a device that builds on the basic compass to include an inclinometer (also called a "clinometers") and a plane-table transit to measure planes and various angles, so it is especially useful as a forestry instrument to measure tree height. It is expensive but serves as three distinct instruments in a compact unit. Rangefinding and inclination are two capacities that have been served by tape measures and inclinometers for the past century as standard forestry instruments for measuring the height of trees. To a great extent, these instruments can be replaced in a field kit (for a fraction of the cost) by a laser rangefinder.

## Tree Measurement and Tagging Equipment

Another simple but useful device is called a "crown densitometer", which measures the percentage of canopy or crown vegetation over a fixed location. This is a spherical mirror with a box grid engraved on its surface, and when used as directed will produce a consistent measure of the overhead obstruction. Most ecological surveys require measurement of the diameter at breast height (DBH) of trees to calculate various indices of tree and food availability. While a regular measuring tape will give you a circumference that you can convert to DBH, specific DBH measuring tapes are excellent for doing the calculation automatically and they have little metal "grips" to help hold the tape on the bark as you measure.

In forests, it is often necessary to "tag" trees for research purposes. The forest industry has developed a large variety of aluminum tags and even aluminum nails for these needs. Ethically, the use of aluminum materials avoids damage to the tree, and if the wood is ever delivered into the hands of sawyers, there is no danger of shattering a powered sawblade—an occurrence that can be fatal to the operators if a steel nail is encountered.

Primatologists may also need to collect ecological samples for laboratory analyses to determine the physical and/or chemical attributes of the food supply as a key component to investigating primate feeding ecology. For more terrestrial species, food can often be collected on the ground or with hand pruners; however, leaves, flowers, or fruits from a feeding tree high in the canopy can be collected using long pruner poles that are adjustable to different lengths. Once collected, the samples must be handled and stored according to best practices for the research you are undertaking. For example, basic nutritional analyses of plant foods require dehydration of the sample in a food dehydrator or freeze-drying in liquid nitrogen if facilities are available. A complete review of methods for ecological analyses is available in Rothman et al. (2012).

## Meteorological Measurement Tools

Most primatologists also need to regularly record a series of meteorological measurements such as daily temperature, rainfall, and perhaps wind speed. A reliable, good-quality temperature gauge mounted in an open area should provide adequate and consistent temperature readings, provided they are read at about the same time/s each day. A version called a "min./max. thermometer" will mark the minimum and maximum temperature for you over 24 hours and just needs to be reset when the data are read. There are also electronic units (often called "weather stations") that are mounted outdoors with sensors that send the temperature data to an indoor unit; however, regular batteries or another power source (depending on the unit) are required. Rainfall and other precipitation can be measured using a rain gauge, which can be manual or automatic. A manual rain gauge collects rainfall (again, mounted in an open area) in a graduated cylinder (which in some cases has an overflow collector), and the water is disposed of once the measurement (generally in mm) is taken. Manual units for the average fieldworker are inexpensive and reliable. An automatic rain gauge has two parts (similar to electronic temperature gauges): an outdoor collecting device of some kind with sensors and an indoor display unit. The sensors transmit the data to the indoor device so that data are logged, and the fieldworker is spared the hassle of having to regularly go outside, read the unit, and dispose of the water. However, like many electronic devices, they have to remain powered with batteries of some kind, which may be difficult to maintain in remote areas. Wind can be measured using handheld wind meters. Kestrel holds much of the market in handheld wind meters, and they have a variety of models available with different features ranging in price from $75–$400 USD (https://kestrelmeters.com).

# Repair Materials

Many things break or wear out during a field study, and while some cannot be repaired by the researcher, many others can be, at least temporarily. Two important materials should always be on hand. Duct tape (also referred to as "duck tape") can hold many things together, provide sealing for packages, emergency bandages, and even serve as tree tags when needed. A high-quality option is gaffer tape, the material used in Hollywood and ubiquitous on movie sets. The second material is a tube or two of "Goop" or another type of flexible, general adhesive, which are available in varieties tailored for use on footwear or as a general household adhesive. These kinds of materials are ideal for sealing tears in boots, patching rain ponchos, sticking up signs at trail intersections, or using on anything, anywhere that adhesive or patching is needed.

---

# Other Considerations

## Transport

In any field research project that involves primates, one of the major expenses is transport to the field, principally because wild primates generally live in tropical and subtropical areas of the world that, in some cases, are far away, remote, and difficult to get to. There are still areas in the primate study world where a "full pack" hike of more than a day is necessary to get to an established research site. If the project requires more gear than can be comfortably carried on your back, there will be additional costs for porters, who will also have to be fed and sheltered in addition to being paid. Most countries have some form of local bus service that varies in quality from good to horrid, and/or taxi services that can help.

That said, primates live in parts of the world where modern transportation is often not what we are used to in many industrialized parts of the world like the U.S. and Canada. A field researcher needs to be patient and flexible in their transportation planning and prepared to tolerate some level of discomfort to get to a field location. Unfortunately, many primates also live in areas of the world that experience ongoing or recurring political instability that may be dangerous for researchers. Consult https://www.state.gov/travelers/ in the U.S., or https://travel.gc.ca/ in Canada for the most updated travel information for your destination. You can register as a citizen abroad and receive a text or email messages regarding any emergencies that are occurring in the region where you are working.

## Disease Prophylaxis/Vaccinations

Fieldwork in tropical conditions involves exposure to a broad range of parasites, bacteria, and viruses that will be new to a temperate zone resident. Many of these will be benign or produce only short term illnesses, but some—malaria, schistosomiasis, onchocerciasis, dengue, yellow fever, chikungunya, and a range of emerging viruses (Lassa, Ebola, Kayasonur, Marburg, Zika, West Nile, Lyme disease, and SARS-CoV-2)—are more serious, dangerous, or even lethal. Volumes could, and have been, written about the various forms of pathogens that fieldworkers can be exposed to. It is not our intent to provide a full list of potential diseases and ways to avoid them. Rather, we provide some general guidelines to stay healthy while undertaking fieldwork, though there are never any guarantees.

Many common but dangerous pathogens are carried by mosquitoes or ticks as vectors; therefore, the most effective prophylaxis against these pathogens is to avoid exposure in the first place. The most basic form of protection is to wear long pants and sleeves (treated with permethrin if possible) and to use mosquito nets and effective insect repellents containing DEET or picaridin. If you are conducting your fieldwork in an area of the world with high incidences of malaria, one of the most prevalent pathogens, most medical professionals will recommend additional prophylaxis specific to the region. Historically, doxycycline (an antibiotic-derived compound) has been prescribed to prevent malaria with minimal side effects, but its efficacy is inconsistent. More effective is the use of mefloquine (sold under the trade name *Lariam*), but there remains great controversy about its side effects as it is not always well tolerated. More recently, *Malarone* (a combination of atovaquone and proguanil) has become the antimalarial drug of choice due to its high efficacy and tolerance with fewer negative side effects, though it tends to be more expensive than the other choices. Different medical associations make different recommendations, and many workers on long-duration projects elect to avoid prophylactic drugs altogether and instead use *Halofan* or *Artemisia* as a treatment when malaria does appear, but this is a risky choice and not recommended. For other emerging infectious diseases such as the Zika and SARS-CoV-2 viruses, the medical and pharmaceutical industries are still investigating the courses of these diseases and the best forms of treatment.

Avoidance of exposure to other parasites, such as *Schistosoma mansoni* and its related species, is the most practical prophylaxis as the treatments for the resulting disease (bilharzia) is dangerous and debilitating. Since the snails that host the infective larval stage live in standing and slow-moving water, exposure can be avoided. In part, schistosomes are the reason all drinking water should be run through a ceramic filter system at a minimum, and preferably boiled before filtering, unless you can be assured that your drinking water source is safe.

Effective prevention of some diseases can be acquired through vaccination. The Centers for Disease Control and Prevention (CDC) recommends beginning vaccinations at least one month before leaving for the field (see https://wwwnc.cdc.gov/travel/page/travel-vaccines for further information), but the lead time can be much longer for certain vaccinations that may require several courses for full efficacy. Vaccinations can keep you healthy while in the field and ensure that you do not bring diseases back to your family, friends, and community when you return home. They are recommended where appropriate and when authorized by your attending physician. Some common vaccinations to consider, depending on where you are conducting your research, are yellow fever, typhoid, hepatitis A and B, rabies, and meningitis. For entry into many African and Central and South American countries, a card declaring that you have received a yellow fever vaccination is necessary (check with the CDC or the government website of the country in question). It is also recommended that you are fully immunized and up-to-date against measles, mumps, rubella, tetanus, diphtheria, pertussis, and seasonal influenza. Consult the World

Health Organization (WHO) https://www.who.int/ith/en/ and the CDC https://www.cdc.gov/vaccines/adults/rec-vac/index.html for further information on what may be right for you. Of course, it is essential to consult with your physician and travel clinician well in advance of travel to discuss the best options for you before undertaking your fieldwork.

An important note: Given our close evolutionary relationship with nonhuman primates, it is recommended that anyone working within reasonable proximity with the study subjects ensure they have recently tested negative for tuberculosis, or have had a clean chest X-ray if they test positive, and have obtained appropriate vaccinations for pathogens their nonhuman primate subjects may be vulnerable to. It is also important to stay home and not expose primates to pathogens if you feel sick while working in the field. If vaccinations or other prophylaxes are limited or not available for prevention of a particular pathogen (as was the case with SARS-CoV-2, the coronavirus that causes COVID-19, at the time of this writing), it is imperative that field workers DO NOT conduct field work and expose subjects to a novel or untreatable pathogen that could wipe out an entire primate population.

## Snakes, Ticks, Scorpions, and Spiders

Beginning fieldworkers are naturally concerned about the dangerous life-forms at their field site, and indeed many snakes, a few scorpions, and some spiders are dangerous enough to warrant serious consideration. Yet, venomous reptiles and insects are not there to make a meal of unsuspecting researchers. Given a choice, they will flee more often than not. The danger level then descends to the few that demonstrate overtly aggressive manners (for example, mambas in Africa, some pit vipers in the Americas), or are so cryptic in their coloration that one can easily but inadvertently step on them, provoking a retaliatory strike.

To protect oneself, at many field sites it is appropriate to wear protective snake leggings, such as the many varieties available from Forestry Suppliers, Inc. Though they can be heavy, stiff, and hot, they should be considered essential gear for some field sites. As mentioned in the gear list above, a snake bite kit can help to extract the venom if someone on the field team is bitten, and they are small, lightweight, and portable so it should be easy to always carry a kit with you. If you are in an area where venomous snakes are common and dangerous to humans, you should keep antivenin appropriate to the species (if available) on hand. This is often supplied in two vials and the task of mixing them and managing the injection into a vein is not for the faint of heart, nor is it something that one wants to do in the field during those shaky moments after having been struck. That said, antivenins are best left in the base camp as they often need refrigeration. If a hospital is nearby, and time allows, the antivenin can be taken there to be injected by a medical professional.

Tick removal devices (or a good pair of tweezers) are also useful in areas or seasons when ticks are prevalent. Scorpions generally have a worse reputation than is warranted. For many species, the sting is no worse than that of a bee or wasp; however, there are a few species that can be dangerous to humans and it is advisable to be aware of those and what they look like if you are conducting research in an area where these species may live.

Of course, the best prophylaxis to avoid dangerous situations is to always be vigilant and aware of your surroundings. This rule applies to all venomous organisms. Many snakes and spiders help us out in this regard as they are brightly colored and beautiful. One of the best ways to avoid snakes, spiders, and bites is to wear closed-toe shoes at night if you must walk between buildings or tents in poorly lit areas. It is also advisable to look before stepping, sitting, or placing your hand anywhere in a tropical forest, as stinging and biting ants are omnipresent.

## Wills

One final matter drives the field researcher into the legal offices. Everyone undertaking field research, whether it is a brief survey or a year in the bush, needs to have a completed legal will on file. This does nothing for the researcher but certainly can make life simpler for family and heirs or offspring. A visit to the lawyer or online legal firm to update your will is an important step before a trip to the field.

---

# Final Thoughts

The conduct of field research in a distant and undisturbed habit may initially sound exotic and inviting, but the realities of the experience can be very different. If one goes off with the expectations that everything will be perfect, that you will have all the appropriate gear and that everything will proceed smoothly from start to finish, then the shock of reality may be unnerving. The truth is, research is not like a fairy tale, things do not always "go right" and the axiom "expect the unexpected" is true more often than not.

All the authors of this book have, in one way or another, had the experience of living through a coup d'état; had broken bones or sprained ankles; been bitten, stung, and damaged by plant and animal life; have seen their research design crash with device failure; and have dealt with subject animals not behaving in any way like they were expected. In short, expect and plan for culture shock, as well as problems with institutional red tape, equipment, materials, and the unexpected behavior of your subjects. Despite the travails of failed grant applications, failed research designs, and all the other irritations, none of us would have chosen a different course for their life. If you choose to take a similar path, we hope it proves as enjoyable and rewarding.

# PART TWO

## Exercises

# Basic Studies
## Preliminaries Necessary to All Research

### EXERCISE 1
Animal Identification: Learning Faces and Bodies

### EXERCISE 2
The Ethogram: A Basic Behavior Inventory

### EXERCISE 3
The Observing Schedule

# EXERCISE 1

# Animal Identification
## Learning Faces and Bodies

A preliminary activity that is essential to the conduct of further research is the process of learning to identify individual animals. While it is ideal to know each animal by their name/label, it may also be sufficient for the research protocol to at least be able to identify individuals at the level of age and sex class categories. It might be assumed that this is an elementary task; that everyone should be able to recognize a male and distinguish one from a female, and likewise, that it is simple to evaluate the age of an animal. However, this is often not the case.

To emphasize the difficulties of distinguishing age-sex classes, we suggest that students visit a nearby zoological facility and attempt to classify different animal species into their age-sex categories. It will soon become apparent that the ability to do this easily is species-dependent. Excellent examples are members of the genus *Ateles*, commonly known as spider monkeys. The usual response of students to the question of which individual is male and which is female, in this genus, will result in embarrassment. Preliminary information is needed for students to understand that males have a retractile penis (i.e., so often none is visible) and the apparent "penis" observed on many animals is actually the enlarged clitoris of the female.

Similarly, in the past, practiced fieldworkers have made substantial errors in assessing the ages of subject animals. This was due to judgment of age based on their experiences and subsequent biases, and not on criteria established over a long period (years) of familiarity with the subject species.

## Identifying Age-Sex Classes

In a zoological park or a primate facility, students can often request a list of the animals in their study groups. These lists typically include information on the obvious visual characteristics of each individual, their sex, their history, and their birth date or suspected year of birth if they were wild-caught.

In studies conducted in the wild, the information available varies greatly. Students starting out within an established research project may benefit from similar documented information on individual animals, depending on how long the project has been going on and its level of detail. However, if you are starting research on a species in the wild where this information is not available, the first place to begin is a thorough search of the literature on the study species or a closely related species. This may tell you what features to look for to differentiate males and females. Are there body size differences in adults? Pelage differences? Are the genitals obviously different? Are there some secondary sexual characteristics that will be obvious? For example, in some species, there has been selection for young males to mimic females to avoid competition with dominant males. Young animals may also have developmental stages where their morphological features change. As an example, in mantled howler monkeys, male testes do not begin to descend until early sexual maturity at 3–4 years of age, so determining sex in infants and juveniles from observation alone is impossible. This type of information is important for a new researcher to know before going out into the field to avoid inaccurate data collection.

In terms of classifying age when no previous information for your study animals is available, the literature may again be useful. However, publications may just state that age classes were defined as infant (not weaned), juvenile (weaned), subadult, and adult based on body size relative to other individuals. This is the usual way that these classifications are made when birth dates are not known. It is wisest for the beginning observer to use broad categories and to be cautious about estimates of age, since individual differences in growth trajectories may exist. Researchers often do not divide the "adult" category into many classes if individual identity is not known. However, old individuals may be evident by phenotypic characters like wrinkles, sagging skin, bent backs, and stiff walks. Age estimates are often done on anesthetized animals by looking at the wear on the teeth. Tooth wear can also sometimes be seen clearly when animals yawn, so students may benefit from an examination of known-age skulls to get to know the degree of dental wear that is typical at certain ages, though students should seek appropriate expertise to guide them.

# Individuality: Recognizing That Not Everyone Is Alike

A key to beginning to recognize individuals is the acceptance that each organism produced from a sexual genetic union is a unique entity, different from all others. Also, it can be recognized that each individual pursues its course through life and will have a unique set of experiences, which may result in accumulated evidence of minor and/or major injuries, resulting in apparent scars, broken fingers or toes, or other distinguishing markings or characteristics. All of these differentiating factors—genetic, ontogenetic, and experiential—contribute to the "identity" of each individual, and it is the responsibility of the observer to seek out and record these distinctive features. It will generally be that these features are physical markings or variations in body structure or scars, but it is not unusual for experienced observers to recognize familiar subject animals at inordinately long distances through some peculiarities of movement pattern or behavioral characteristics such as posture or carriage pattern. One of the easiest characteristics to discern is a limb, hand, or foot stiffness caused by a healed fracture.

In many captive care facilities and with some free-ranging populations it has become common practice to apply some form of tattooing or hair-shave pattern to provide individual identification. A code system for facial tattoos is an occasional complement to Arabic numbers applied on a low hair density area such as the inner thigh or abdomen. Such codes like the one employed on the Arashiyama A and B troops (South Texas and Arashiyama Mountain, Kyoto respectively) are not intuitively obvious and a researcher must be trained in their reading. In natural circumstances, various devices such as collars, ear tags, and ankle tags have been employed as identification tools, but have the major handicap of requiring that the animal be captured and sedated for their installation, nor are they permanent. In the end, most workers forego these extravagances and learn to identify individuals using natural characteristics. Since zoological facilities are unlikely to countenance manipulation of their charges, students will also have to learn individual natural features.

# The Exercise

The purpose of this exercise is to develop skills at individual recognition and identification as well as to produce a set of primate identification cards sufficiently characterized that another observer could recognize the subjects from the material. It is estimated that this project should take between one and two hours to complete.

A.  Select a subject group of primates. It is suggested that these should be a larger species such as a macaque, guenon, baboon, or an ape group. The group must consist of at least 3 animals. The reason for not suggesting a small primate such as a marmoset or squirrel monkey lies in their pattern and rapidity of movement, factors that would make it difficult for a first-time observer to obtain appropriate information.

B.  Examine the face and body of each individual for several minutes, paying attention to relative features that may serve to distinguish between individuals. Are there differences in sizes, overall dimensions; are there differences in the sizes of specific regions or areas; are there differences in the hair coat (pelage) in terms of lengths on different regions, in color patterns; or are there variations in skin (dermis) coloration or patterning? Are there any obvious scars or limb, hand, or foot damage? These types of distinctions will serve as the basis for the identification of individuals.

C. Using the "identification sheets" (either use copies of the examples here, or print out sufficient numbers of the correct form from the supplementary material provided on this text's webpage at **waveland.com**), fill in the appropriate data on the top of the sheet, and using the face schematics on the bottom draw in the locations, sizes, and shapes of relevant pigmentation spots, tattoo marks, scars, other blemishes, or similar identifying features. It is undesirable to attempt to generate a perfect likeness of the subject; what is necessary are the key features that distinguish him or her from others, and consequently, these can be schematic (examine the sample identification sheet provided on the facing page).

D. The sheet has space for the observer's identity, the subject's identity (this may be the name used by the keepers, or it may be created by you as an aid to identification), group observed in, date of observation, age and sex evaluation, and where known, the genealogical relationship of the subject. A further set of physical characteristics that may serve to separate this subject from others is also to be recorded. Take note of ear color and major notches (some primates such as lemurs are often easier to identify by their ear notches—features produced during fights—than by other characteristics). The remainder of the sheet is available for other data.

A sample layout of the record sheet with an example is provided on the next page. The following pages provide blank versions for different kinds of primates that can be copied to conduct the exercise. These sheets can also be printed as cards to be used in a permanent file. This design is based on a card suggested in Appendix C of *Techniques for the Study of Primate Population Ecology* (National Research Council 1981).

**General Monkey Identification Sheet: Worked Example**

Observer: <u>J. D. Paterson</u> Card Date: <u>92/5/16</u> Species: <u>M. fusc</u> Record #: <u>074</u>

Location: <u>STPO</u> Group: <u>Arashiyama A (main)</u> Sex: ☒ M ☐ F

Subject ID Code: <u>Rotte 70</u> Familiar Name: <u>Fang</u>

Age: ☐ Old Adult ☒ Prime Adult ☐ Young Adult ☐ Subadult ☐ Juvenile

☐ Infant One ☐ Infant Two ☐ Infant Three

Age Today: <u>21</u> Birth Date: <u>1970/5</u> Mother: <u>Rotte</u> Lineage: <u>Rotte</u>

Coloration: Body Hair: <u>Honey</u> Body Skin: <u>Light blue</u> Ear: <u>Tan</u>

Head Hair: <u>Brown</u> Face: <u>Light pink</u> Perineum: <u>Pale</u>

Scars and Damage: Ears: <u>None</u> Head: <u>Cleft palate</u> Limbs: <u>None</u>

Social Rank in Sexed Hierarchy: <u>#2</u> in Lineage: <u>Sole member</u>

Other Morphological

Eyes blue, exposed molars on left, large body size

Other Social

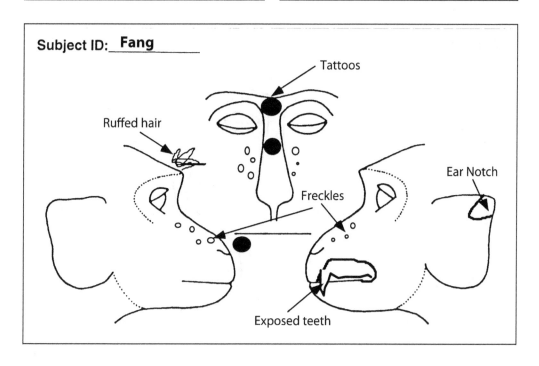

Subject ID: **Fang**

Tattoos

Ruffed hair

Freckles

Ear Notch

Exposed teeth

**Catarrhine Monkey Identification Sheet: Blank**

Observer: _____ Card Date: _____ Species: _____ Record #: _____

Location: _____ Group: _____ Sex: ❏ M  ❏ F

Subject ID Code: _____ Familiar Name: _____

Age:  ❏ Old Adult  ❏ Prime Adult  ❏ Young Adult  ❏ Subadult  ❏ Juvenile

   ❏ Infant One  ❏ Infant Two  ❏ Infant Three

Age Today: _____ Birth Date: _____ Mother: _____ Lineage: _____

Coloration: Body Hair: _____ Body Skin: _____ Ear: _____

   Head Hair: _____ Face: _____ Perineum: _____

Scars and Damage: Ears: _____ Head: _____ Limbs: _____

Social Rank in Sexed Hierarchy: _____ in Lineage: _____

Other Morphological                    Other Social

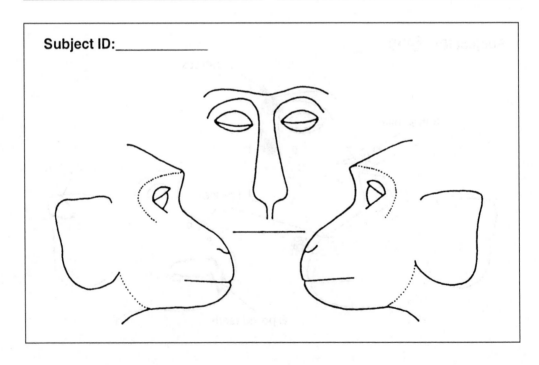

**Subject ID:_____**

## Great Ape Identification Sheet

Observer: _____ Card Date: _____ Species: _____ Record #: _____

Location: _____ Group: _____ Sex: ❏ M  ❏ F

Subject ID Code: _____ Familiar Name: _____

Age:  ❏ Old Adult  ❏ Prime Adult  ❏ Young Adult  ❏ Subadult  ❏ Juvenile
      ❏ Infant One  ❏ Infant Two  ❏ Infant Three

Age Today: _____ Birth Date: _____ Mother: _____ Lineage: _____

Coloration: Body Hair: _____ Body Skin: _____ Ear: _____

                 Head Hair: _____ Face: _____ Perineum: _____

Scars and Damage: Ears: _____ Head: _____ Limbs: _____

Social Rank in Sexed Hierarchy: _____ in Lineage: _____

Other Morphological

Other Social

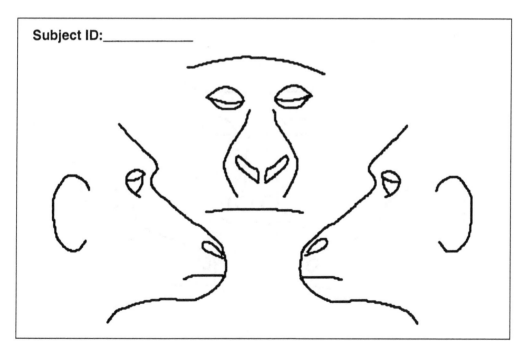

**Subject ID:** _____

**Lemur Identification Sheet**

Observer: _____ Card Date: _____ Species: _____ Record #: _____

Location: _____ Group: _____ Sex: ❑ M  ❑ F

Subject ID Code: _____ Familiar Name: _____

Age:    ❑ Old Adult  ❑ Prime Adult  ❑ Young Adult  ❑ Subadult  ❑ Juvenile

      ❑ Infant One  ❑ Infant Two  ❑ Infant Three

Age Today: _____ Birth Date: _____ Mother: _____ Lineage: _____

Coloration: Body Hair: _____ Body Skin: _____ Ear: _____

           Head Hair: _____ Face: _____ Perineum: _____

Scars and Damage: Ears: _____ Head: _____ Limbs: _____

Social Rank in Sexed Hierarchy: _____ in Lineage: _____

Other Morphological

Other Social

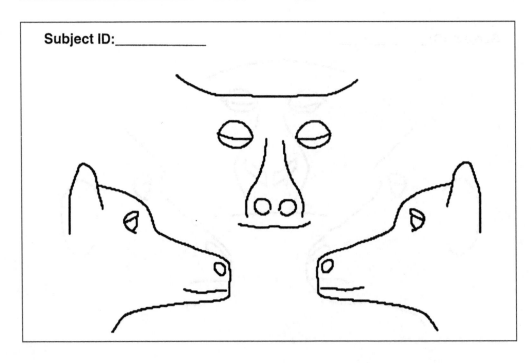

Subject ID:_____

142

**Platyrrhine Identification Sheet**

Observer: _____ Card Date: _____ Species: _____ Record #: _____

Location: _____ Group: _____ Sex: ❏ M ❏ F

Subject ID Code: _____ Familiar Name: _____

Age:  ❏ Old Adult  ❏ Prime Adult  ❏ Young Adult  ❏ Subadult  ❏ Juvenile
      ❏ Infant One  ❏ Infant Two  ❏ Infant Three

Age Today: _____ Birth Date: _____ Mother: _____ Lineage: _____

Coloration:  Body Hair: _____ Body Skin: _____ Ear: _____

             Head Hair: _____ Face: _____ Perineum: _____

Scars and Damage:  Ears: _____ Head: _____ Limbs: _____

Social Rank in Sexed Hierarchy: _____ in Lineage: _____

Other Morphological                          Other Social

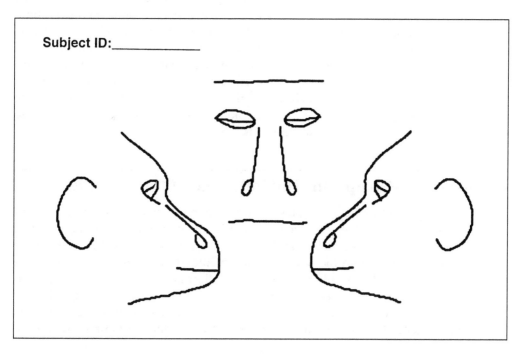

Subject ID:_____

143

# Exercise 2

# The Ethogram
## A Basic Behavior Inventory

The concept of an "ethogram" is central to the study of animal behavior but is perhaps one of the more difficult tasks to operationalize. As discussed in chapter 3, an ethogram is a catalog of an animal's behavioral repertoire, essentially a listing of the forms of behavior displayed by the animal. Unfortunately, complete ethograms do not exist for most primates, despite many years of effort. Part of the problem is that it takes a long period of observation—typically, thousands of hours—to produce a nearly complete catalog. However, it is generally expected that about 90% of a species' ethogram can be obtained in approximately 100 hours of observation, and it is possible to obtain at least some idea of the potential behavioral range of a species in just a few hours of observation.

Information on a species' behavioral repertoire can also be at least partially generated (in many cases) from the available literature. From a practical perspective, most ethograms represent a combination of finer-grained and broad behaviors, depending on the research questions being addressed, but should cover all potential behaviors (in some way) that will be observed. The ethogram listing so produced, and the skills developed for doing so, will figure significantly in the other exercises in this book.

## Behavior and Perception: The Influence of the Observer

It is important for beginning researchers to remind themselves that a behavior record of the activities of subject animals is a mental construct of the observer, and as such is subject to bias and distortion that may divorce the reality of the subject's action from the perceived and recorded observations. Many people only see what they want to see, even when they are trying to be "objective." It is also important to recognize that this situation can become significantly worse if the observer is fatigued. It is not just the visual system that may be influenced, observations may also depend on auditory information, adding another processing system that may be affected by fatigue. Students can refer to the information presented in chapters 2 and 3 to aid in the control of such perceptual biases.

## The Exercise

One of the major issues to address in compiling an appropriate ethogram is to formulate discrete categories of behavior with as few cases (preferably none) of overlap as possible. The purpose of this exercise is to learn to perceive and categorize the behavior of primate subjects in a captive, controlled environment. Secondarily, the exercise provides practice at constructing definitions, an activity that is central to any study of behavior.

Observational and exercise procedures are as follows:

A. Select a single individual of a single species as the subject. The subject should be a moderately active individual. Too inactive and there will not be much activity or variation of behavior to observe, too active and it may be impossible to keep up with the behavior records without losing data.

B. Observe the subject for a period of two or three hours (your instructor may specify more or less time for this exercise). It may be advisable to take at least 30 minutes or so to familiarize yourself with the subject group and their activity patterns before selecting a subject and beginning the formal study.

C. Record each of the activities of the subject during the period. Activities should be easily recognized categories with (more or less) identifiable functions. Once a particular activity is seen, it need not be repeated in the record unless it reflects a change from active to passive or *vice versa*, or is changed in form.

D. Watch and note the details of each of the activities and try to recognize the identifying or diagnostic features of each, i.e., those features that make behaviors distinguishable from one another.

E. Write up definitions based on these detailed descriptions as formal definitions of each behavior unit. Beware of the cardinal rule of definition: A term may not be described using the term being defined. It is not acceptable to define sleeping as "the activity of sleeping" but, rather, as "remaining in a relaxed posture with closed eyes, regular breathing and apparent unconsciousness." These units are perhaps best described in the form of an abbreviated "atomic" description of the actions that constitute the unit, i.e., the fine details of behavior constituted by individual muscle movements and skeletal actions.

The results can be presented as a short report or as a labeled list. A basic form is included on the book's webpage at waveland.com and, at the discretion of the instructor, may be used for completion of this exercise.

How many different behaviors were you able to find in your study? It would take a very active subject and close observation to find more than thirty distinct behaviors in such an initial study, but you should be aware that an ethogram for baboons (*Papio cynocephalus*) produced by Coelho and Bramblett (1990) counts almost 200 distinct behaviors at their molecular level.

# EXERCISE 3

# The Observing Schedule

An observing schedule provides you with a systematic and (largely) unbiased approach to conducting your observations and is an important preliminary to the conduct of any project that involves controlled sampling. As noted in chapter 2, there are two forms of observing schedule: fixed and random schedules. Consequently, this exercise involves the production of both types of schedule.

Several of the techniques in the exercise set do not require a schedule since there is no requirement for equality of sample sizes or "stationarity" (i.e., a time series where properties like mean, variance, autocorrelation, and other measures are constant over time) in the data for the statistics used in their analyses. However, other protocols do require either or both of these features for a valid analysis to be produced. Interval sampling can fall into both categories: instantaneous scan samples, as repeated slices of behavioral time in a group, do not require scheduling, but focal time samples, as repeated slices of behavioral time for one individual at a time, do require scheduling. The most frequently employed system, continuous recording of individual behaviors for fixed periods—focal animal sampling—is the protocol most in need of schedules.

## The Exercise

### Fixed Format Schedule

The student is first directed to the section on fixed format scheduling in chapter 2, and will then set up a schedule of observing for the following project.

A population of spider monkeys, *Ateles paniscus*, resides in a large outdoor enclosure 20 x 20 m and 10 m high, at the local zoological park. The group consists of one adult male, three adult females of differing ages, four juveniles (three female, one male), and two older infants. The facility is open all year round from dawn to dusk, and the variation in day length is limited (14 hours at midsummer, 10 hours at midwinter).

A study of 14 days total duration is planned, with approximately one week scheduled for midsummer and another for midwinter. The observing protocol employed is to be half-hour (30 minutes) focal animal samples. The observer feels that a 5-minute rest after two samples is appropriate and that a 6-hour, 12-sample working day is all that is possible. The sample sizes must be equal for all animals, and for each of the study periods. Questions appropriate to this task are:

1. How many hours are available for the study? How are they distributed? How will the working days be distributed between the two study periods?

2. What is the influence of the rest periods on the sampling schedule? What alterations would adjust the schedule to make it more uniform? Is it necessary?

The tasks for this exercise are to:

1. Construct schedules (a row and column table with codes for individuals is appropriate) for the summer and winter study periods.

2. Construct schedules with your choice of an alteration in the observing protocol in agreement with question 2 above.

3. Construct schedules for two observers working on the project and attempt to maximize the amount of observation time.

You should end with six schedule tables. A blank sample schedule sheet is included online at waveland.com.

## Random Sampling Schedule

The student is first directed to the section on random scheduling in chapter 2, and will then set up a schedule of observing for the following project.

A population of 36 identified individual olive baboons, *Papio anubis*, is to be the subject of an intensive study in the woodland savanna near the edge of the Albertine Rift in western Uganda. The observing protocol has been decided as 15-minute focal animal samples followed by a five-minute rest and search period, with the observer putting in a 12-hour field day. The study is intended to be one full year in duration.

The tasks for this exercise are to:

1. Using either a set of strips numbered 1 through 36, or a pair of cubic dice (see below for instructions on how to operate this process) construct an observing sequence for a six-day working week.

2. Total up the numbers of samples for each animal in the study population to see how often each individual is studied during the week. Is the distribution equitable? How many subjects were not to be observed at all during this particular week?

Random sample generation using dice is not as simple as the use of numbered slips. Since the most common die is the cube with numbers from 1 to 6, it requires a stratified process for any larger group. The simplest technique is to divide the entire group into 6 parts, and for large groups, each of these may be divided into further 6 parts. At that point, it is possible to start rolling the dice. In the case above, with 36 individuals, two dice can be used. The first die selects the partition and the second selects the individual within the partition (to keep it clear the dice should be of differing colors). For example, if the first die comes up with a 3, it selects the third partition, i.e., individuals who are numbered 13 through 18; and if the second die also turns up 3, the third individual in the set is selected—number 15. The die readings themselves do not indicate individuals unless there is equivalence between the number of subjects and the number of faces on the die. Role-playing dice with up to 20 faces exist and could be used in place of the stratified process, but with higher numbers, one is again faced with the need for stratification of the process. Since each selection of a partition depends on the random turn of the die, the end result is a true random selection of a subject.

Remember that a reserve list should also be generated to cover cases where the target cannot be located for that sample period.

# Group Comparative Studies
## To Develop an Appreciation
## of the Differences Between Species

### EXERCISE 4
The Behavior Profile: A Comparative Study

### EXERCISE 5
Time Budget: A State Behavior Duration Exercise

# EXERCISE 4

# The Behavior Profile
## A Comparative Study

The behavior profile is a study technique appropriate to the usual settings of a zoo environment and is designed to produce a direct comparison between two or more species of animals. As outlined below, the technique is simple but effective; however, the concept and construction of an ethogram as outlined in chapter 3, and executed in exercise 2, is an important prerequisite. There is a degree of similarity between this exercise and exercise 5 on time budgets; however, the purpose of this exercise is oriented toward observing the differences in the *frequencies* and *relative frequencies* of behaviors, not in the time durations of each.

The behavior profile exercise requires that the observer begins with the construction of an arbitrary ethogram; alternatively, the ethogram from exercise 2 can serve as the basis for this project. In either case, the ethogram should be general and limited to a few categories, certainly no more than eight or 10. It is important to use categories of behavior that the student feels will adequately describe the activities of the subjects in each of the comparative groups/species. These behavior categories are to be constructed and defined as "states" for this exercise, even though they will be treated as events in the data collection and analysis. An appropriate example for an ethogram would include broad categories of behavior, such as locomoting, resting, feeding, agonistic social interaction, affiliative social interaction, and reproductive behavior, with definitions of each left up to the observer. Note that these are not an exclusive or required set of behaviors, and the construction of other sets is encouraged.

Each initiation of these states, i.e., each change of behavior from one to another, during a fixed observation period is recorded. This is a recording method close to the "all occurrences" sampling technique referred to by Altmann (1974). For the analysis, the frequencies of each behavior in each species are calculated. Note that this pattern is one of the variations in the treatment of behavior "states" in that they can be either handled as durational data or counted as occurrences as if they were "events." While this type of treatment loses some information, in practice what is lost is no more than with some other data gathering methods.

## The Exercise

The observational procedure is as follows:

A. Select between two and four different species of primates on which to conduct the study. Each of the species should have groups of comparable size, but this is not a rigid requirement as in many cases it is not practical, depending on the size of the zoo where you are conducting the exercise. A difference of one or two individuals should not be significant in larger groups but if very small groups are compared with very large groups, any variation you find could be due to group size rather than true species differences.

B. Use a watch, stopwatch, or mobile device to time a fixed observational period for each species; 15, 30, or 60 minutes for each is suggested as appropriate, or as selected by the instructor.

C. Record all occurrences of the onset or beginning of each of the behaviors taking place within the enclosure. This means that all members of the group are being scanned, but attention is focused on behaviors, and the changes of behavior, not on individual animals. However, you must keep track of individual animals to accurately record the onset of behavior changes. Note that behaviors that are "continuing" are only counted once, not repeatedly.

Observational Hint: The simplest method is to record a "tick" in the appropriate check-sheet column at the onset of the specified behavior category, irrespective of which animal of the group does it. If two animals engage in a fight, then two ticks are recorded, if three animals begin resting over five minutes, then three ticks go into the resting category, and so on.

D. Repeat the fixed observation period for each species group. Once the data have been collected from all species for the same periods, add up the counts for each category and the totals for each species.

E. Prepare a brief report. This report should include a written component summarizing the methods, results, and discussion. At a minimum, the report should also include a data table showing the frequencies and relative frequencies of behaviors, with rates of occurrence in either frequency per minute or per hour, whichever provides the most readable values. A column or bar graph of either relative frequencies or rates must also be included.

To aid in getting started, a sample check-sheet using the ethogram list suggested above is provided as a model, and is available online.

# Example Check-Sheet for Behavioral Profile

Observer: _____ Date: _____ Time: _____

Sample Duration: _____ Location: _____

Species 1: _____ Species 2: _____

Species 3: _____ Species 4: _____

| Behavior | Species 1 | Species 2 | Species 3 | Species 4 |
|---|---|---|---|---|
| Locomoting | | | | |
| Resting | | | | |
| Feeding | | | | |
| Scanning | | | | |
| Aggressive Interaction | | | | |
| Peaceful Interaction | | | | |
| Grooming Interaction | | | | |
| Sexual Act | | | | |

# EXERCISE 5

# Time Budget
## A State Behavior Duration Exercise

The time budget exercise is related to an important type of research conducted on wild primates; determining how a primate, individually or as part of a group, divides up the daylight hours. Time budgets (also often called "activity budgets") can tell researchers a lot about an animal's ecological and behavioral adaptations. There are a finite number of hours in the day and certain activities must be performed, which limits the time available to perform other activities. The way that animals choose to fill their time is known as their time budget and represents the priority of resource utilization in the activities of making a living.

Dunbar et al. (2009) have argued that time limitations are crucial for determining where certain species are geographically distributed and how large their groups will grow. While eating a large quantity of a poor-quality food source may allow a species to live in a certain area, they may not be able to expand their foraging time sufficiently to take in the amount of food they need, while still performing other essential activities. This means that this species will be unable to live in that particular area. Similarly, if a certain amount of social interaction is required among individuals in a species with intense social bonding, this may limit group size because infinite time is not available for social behavior. Additionally, there may be a trade-off between social time and foraging time, which affects the geographic range. The need for a certain amount of social behavior may limit where a species can survive because they cannot give this up to increase foraging time for poor-quality foods (Dunbar et al. 2009).

The amount of time that a primate spends in feeding and foraging activities is governed by factors that are to some extent species specific and related to the ecological situation. These factors include such things as:

1. Absolute size—a larger primate needs more food than a smaller one but that need is scaled "allometrically" such that larger forms display an increase in energy efficiency.

2. The type of food that the species feeds on—animal sources have the highest concentration of available necessary proteins but are energetically costly to obtain; plant starches are easily locatable, but can be energetically expensive to digest; and fruits are intermediate to both but are only sporadically available.

3. The distribution of the required foods within the environment—some are patchily distributed in clusters while others are uniformly and/or sparsely scattered across the environment, thus dictating different searching strategies.

4. Seasonality—many primates live in highly seasonal environments and can be extremely active during one season and significantly less so in another. For example, Lisa Corewyn found that the mantled howler monkeys (*Alouatta palliata*) at La Pacifica are considerably more active in the wet versus the dry seasons (unpublished data).

Extracting energy from food and searching for food in the environment are time-dependent processes. If a primate species feeds on fruits, its digestive processes tend to run "fast" to extract relatively fewer but higher energy nutrients from its foods. Fruits also tend to be in discrete patches, so the frugivore must move between patches frequently. Conversely, leaf-eaters must spend a great deal of time processing their foods since they depend in some measure on specialized digestive anatomy and/or symbiotic bacteria to extract the low amounts of energy in the cellulose and hemicellulose portions of plant structures. Leaves also tend to be in larger patches than fruits, sometimes allowing folivores to stay in a certain tree longer. As a consequence, fruit eaters tend to be much more active and engage in foraging to a greater extent than leaf-eaters who spend a greater amount of their time resting and digesting. An appropriate analogy is the difference between a banquet where the guests sit in one place eating and digesting, and a buffet where they are continually returning to sample the available delicacies, interspersing periods of feeding and moving.

In a similar fashion, the locomotor activity patterns of primates are to a great extent controlled by the amounts of available energy, the ambient temperatures, and the immediate social environment. This varies for every individual within the society, consequently the time budget for one individual is rarely coincident with that for any other individual; however, in cohesive groups many group members are usually engaged in similar activities at approximately the same time.

Often, one of the most surprising findings for students of primate behavior is the amount of time that the study subjects spend sitting around doing nothing. To some extent, this "surprise" is a product of the video and films utilized to show primate behavior. These are selected and edited from the available footage to illustrate the *active* behavior of the species, and, hence, they tend to produce a false impression of the amounts of time spent by the subjects in various activities. This is perfectly understandable as no one would sit still and watch three or four hours of film of a primate sleeping, yet fieldworkers often find themselves performing that type of activity. For example, James Paterson once spent five-and-a-half hours in a Mexican rain forest with a solitary sub-adult male howler (*Alouatta palliata mexicana*), who slept the whole time and only provided four records of change in posture. The cautionary message is: Do not assume too much about the activity pattern of individual primates, and especially do not rely on media-derived impressions.

Due to the differences in time budgets that arise because of certain adaptations, the ecological environment, group sizes, and/or the needs of an individual, it is informative and advantageous to be able to compare time budgets. However, this can be difficult. As Box (1984) has stated it is

> difficult to obtain accurate measures of time budgets. It is difficult to compare directly results obtained by different methods of estimation. Apart from methodological constraints, studies which have used the same methods of estimation have shown that different populations of the same species have varying patterns of activities in different ecological conditions. (Box 1984:15)

While Box is correct that the problem is complex and that it is difficult to compare across populations, let alone species, the basic concept of a time budget remains valid, particularly for data collected in the same manner by the same researcher. This suggests that, when treated with care and understanding of the constraints on the protocol, there is sufficient internal consistency to make time budgets useful.

One issue that needs to be considered carefully to ensure that time budgets are valid is that the method of data collection is not biased in any way. This means ensuring that "out-of-sight" time is noted as such. In addition, certain behaviors should not be more likely to be recorded than others. For example, Julie Teichroeb collected the time budget of wild white-thighed colobus (*Colobus vellerosus*) during her master's research using a nonbiased scan-sampling technique from dawn to dusk and found a budget of 59% resting, 24% feeding, 14% moving, 3% social behavior (Teichroeb et al. 2003). During her PhD research on the same population using focal-animal sampling, the time budget was found to be much different with 75% resting, 22% feeding, 1% moving, and 2% social behavior (Teichroeb and Sicotte 2009). The large overestimate of resting and underestimate of moving in this sample was due to the data collection technique. While useful for other questions, focal-animal sampling was not appropriate to collect accurate time budget data in this population because these wild, arboreal monkeys are often lost when they move during focal samples. With high out-of-sight times, the samples have to be discarded, leading to reduced moving/traveling from the larger behavioral record. Some other examples of time budget studies that might be useful for students can be found in Defler (1995), Menon and Poirier (1996), and Kurup and Kumar (1993).

# The Exercise

This exercise takes the observer through the activity of conducting a brief time budget study of at least 3 hours duration. To complete properly, such a basic study would normally take a minimum of one full day for each member of the study group; therefore, instructors may make substantial changes in the hours required for this project depending on available time and resources.

The technique of conducting the study is straightforward. Basically, an ethogram of behavior "state" categories that reflect gross activity and energetic cycles is constructed. The traditional set of behavior categories used and advocated by many researchers for comparative use consists of Rest, Move, Feed, Social, and Other (Out-of-sight is also usually added as a behavior category). This list is sometimes reduced even further to Rest, Move, Feed, and Other, but may be expanded for specific purposes (as will be seen below).

Then on a record sheet, record the onset (start times) of all activities as they occur. All of the behavior categories must be defined in such a way that they are mutually exclusive, thus avoiding the possibility of two activities being recorded simultaneously. This exercise can be done with a small group of animals (3 to 5 individuals) using a check-sheet set up with columns for each subject and using a simple code (R, M, F, S, O or R, M, F, O) and the time of the activity start. This process can be tiring and is probably best broken up into 15-, 30-, or 60-minute sessions.

An alternative methodology (employed in Form A2 of the exercise), and one that is essential for a group larger than 3 or 4, would be to focus on individual animals either for fixed duration samples at specific hours on equivalent days or through the development of a random sampling schedule. These options, however, would require increased observation time (3 hours times the number of group members). In either case, a variation of the check-sheet suggested in the scan sampling exercise (exercise 6) is available, and a version of this can be found with the supplementary material provided with this book.

Since the onset of one activity will also be the offset (end time) of the previous behavior, it is not generally necessary to record offsets (a good reason to define the categories as mutually exclusive). The categories used should be capable of reflecting as near to 100% of the time spent observing as is possible. At the end of the observations, it is a simple procedure to calculate the percentage of time spent by the individual subjects (or by each age-sex category) for each of the activities. This reflects the time budget of the sample population. The formula can be stated as:

$$\frac{\text{Total Time in Activity}}{\text{Total Sample Time}} \times 100 = \text{Percentage Time}$$

The results should be presented as a standard, written scientific report although a brief report format may be specified by the instructor. It is advisable to conduct some library research and include a list of references used in either case.

## Exercise Form A

This form of the exercise requires 3 hours minimum study time and the use of a check-sheet for parallel observation of 3 to 5 individuals. The ethogram used should be either the RMFSO or the RMFO versions. If it is possible for the animals to go out-of-sight in the enclosure where they are being studied, this category should also be added to account for the time when you do not know what the individuals are doing. The start time and code for each behavior change is noted in the column for each subject and the sample should continue for 15, 30, or 60 minutes. Breaks should be taken after each sample session.

## Exercise Form A2

Form A2 of the exercise is the same as Form A, but employing the focal animal sampling procedure. This means that observation focuses on one individual subject at a time for a period of time (same sample durations as above). The sample size (number of individuals) for this version is expected to be larger than in Form A.

## Exercise Form B

Form B of the exercise requires the use of a more extensive ethogram. The behavior listing can be as extensive as student and instructor agree on but must consist only of state behaviors—all event behaviors can be lumped under the category of Other. The ethogram list with definitions should be presented as part of the report. As in Form A, parallel observation of 3 to 5 individuals for 3 hours is required.

## Exercise Form B2

Similar to Form A2, Form B2 exercise is based on Form B. The requirement is for an extended listing of state behaviors (with a presentation of the ethogram definitions), but employing focal animal sampling procedures. The group used is expected to be larger and the time involved in the study will be more extensive.

## The Report

Irrespective of which form of the exercise or whether a brief or full report is required, all papers should include the following components.

- The date of your study—not the date of writing it up
- The duration of the study, or if it is broken up into random or scheduled samples on individuals, the duration of each sample, and the total sample time
- Species name and the figures for the group composition
- The behavior categories used and their definitions

- Presentation of a summarization table of your data collection (this should include the duration of sample time for each age-sex class studied, and the percentage of that classes' total time, for each category of behavior)
- A graphic presentation of % time for some subset of age or sex or age-sex categories
- A discussion of the data presented
- Presentation of any conclusions that you have reached about the time budget of the species you have studied (this is the place to confirm or deny any hypotheses or conclusions that you may have found in the literature, but be sure to take some cognizance of the differences between natural and captive conditions)

# Example Check-Sheet for Time Budget

Observer: _____ Date: _____

Subject Group: _____ # in group: _____

Start Time: _____ Group Composition: _____

| Time | Subject 1 | Subject 2 | Subject 3 | Subject 4 | Subject 5 |
|------|-----------|-----------|-----------|-----------|-----------|
|      |           |           |           |           |           |
|      |           |           |           |           |           |
|      |           |           |           |           |           |
|      |           |           |           |           |           |
|      |           |           |           |           |           |
|      |           |           |           |           |           |
|      |           |           |           |           |           |

# Major Modes of Observational Methods
## Learning to Sample Effectively

# EXERCISE 6

# Scan Sampling
## Instantaneous Scan Sampling of States of Behavior, or Interval Sampling

The process of scan sampling, often called "interval sampling," can be considered as analogous to the repeated sweeps of an air traffic controller's radar screen. In much the same way, a "sweep" across the members of the subject group is made, and an instantaneous observation of the state of behavior displayed by each subject individual is recorded. *Theoretically*, this sweep is conducted in zero time and the data collected is then considered to reflect the behavior of the group at a precise slice in time. *Practically*, however, it does take a few seconds to complete the scan, but since it is assumed to be instantaneous, observers should attempt to perform a scan as quickly as possible and yet take sufficient time to retain accuracy. This technique is most frequently oriented to describing group and subgroup (e.g., age-sex class) behavior rather than individual behavior since it takes time to identify individuals. This assumes that the group is a large one. In a small group, such as is typical of zoological collections, it can be functional at the individual level as well, on the condition that the individuals are clearly recognizable and can always be identified during the scan.

As a research method, scan sampling is particularly suited for dealing with activity cycle studies where it can be used to generate an estimate of "percentage of time engaged in specific activities." Thus, it is excellent for time budget studies. It is not a suitable technique for the study of inter-individual interactions as these tend to occur in sequences that cannot be adequately sampled. It also misses nearly all of the short duration (event) and infrequent behaviors. One appropriate use of scan sampling with captive primates is to determine the pattern of preferential usage of various areas in the enclosure (see exercise 19).

# Required Conditions for Scan Sampling

The use of scan sampling techniques must be appropriate to the research design of the study, and the particular types of data to be collected. The behavior to be observed must be of the "state" form, the individual members of the group must be identifiable to at least age and sex class (in small groups it should be to individual level), and the behavior categories must be familiar to and easily recognized by the observer. In cases where these conditions are not consistently present, as when a particular behavior is not perceptible to the observer immediately, a degree of bias is developed, which can distort the results. To minimize problems, the scans should be performed in as consistent a manner as possible throughout the study.

Since the most common end use of scan sampling is to produce a percentage estimate (either frequency or duration) of activity or location, the interval periods of the scans are important. The closer the scans are to one another, the closer the estimate can come to achieving a measure of the "real" time use pattern. To have any reasonable degree of confidence in the validity of this method for real-time estimates, it is necessary that the scans be no more than 10 seconds apart, and preferably only 2 or 5 seconds. There are intervening factors such as timing control, the type of activity, the size of the group, and the difficulty of behavioral unit recognition or individual subject identification, which will dictate the functional minimum periods between scans. Researchers often use intervals of 15, 20, or 30 seconds between scans and a common accessory is a timer equipped with a beeper to provide precise control over the scanning rate. Most phones and digital watches have "pacer" or "timer" functions that can be set to operate in the same fashion. The time between scans that works for your particular study group can be determined by testing out several intervals to see what is functionally possible before you begin to collect real data.

# Correction of the Out-of-Sight Problem

As mentioned in chapter 2, one of the significant problems that can develop in a short study is the "out-of-sight" situation. This is particularly important in this exercise since out-of-sight records for particular individuals or age-sex classes will significantly bias the results. This biasing will be particularly evident due to the short time of the study. It would tend to even out and become less of a biasing factor if a hundred or more hours of sampling were being done.

To deal with the out-of-sight problem in this exercise, the observer has a set of options available. The first is obvious but disheartening: throw out the sample as soon as an animal goes out-of-sight and begin again. A partial solution that avoids this scenario would be to conduct the exercise on a warm sunny afternoon rather than a cool damp or rainy morning as there would be a greater probability of completing the exercise with all animals visible. The second option is to suspend scans while any animal is out-of-sight and then continue once all subjects are visible again. This would allow the collection of a complete sample, but as discussed in chapter 2, it may introduce unknown and uncontrollable biases into the data. It is, however, an acceptable choice in this exercise. The third option involves two stages, the data must be collected in the standard format, but if any individual animal is absent from view for more than one-third of the samples, the sample must be redone. The second stage involves a correction ("a fudge factor" to some) that is applied to the data set. This correction assumes that at least two-thirds of the sample has all subjects present, and the calculations are based only on those scans. Effectively, one removes the complete scan where an animal is out-of-sight. If this means the exercise ends with 143 valid scans instead of 160, the calculations of rate and percentage will be influenced if uncorrected. For example, if feeding occurs 34 times in the whole sample, the calculations would be:

for 160 scans  34/160 = .2125 as the rate per scan
34/160 x 100 = 21.25% (percent of scans where feeding occurred)

for 143 scans  34/143 = .2378 as the rate per scan
34/143 x 100 = 23.78% (percent of scans where feeding occurred)

To calculate the rate per hour or the rate per minute in the same situations, the following calculations would take place:

for 160 scans or 40 minutes
34/40 = .85 per minute
34/40 x 60 = 51 instances of feeding per hour

for 143 scans or 35.75 minutes
34/35.75 = .951 instances of feeding per minute
34/35.75 x 60 = 57.06 instances of feeding per hour

The use of percentages and corrected calculations for scan sampling is the most appropriate mechanism to improve the accuracy of the data summarizations.

Discrepancies in the sex ratio (the numbers of males and females in the group) and the age make-up (the numbers of adults, subadults, juveniles, and infants) will also have some biasing effect on the overall group frequencies and rates of behaviors. Data can be averaged for each age-sex class and converted to percentages to compare behaviors among these categories of individuals; however, large numbers of scans are needed if data are to be divided this way. For the exercise below, issues related to the sex ratio and age make-up of the study group can be ignored.

# The Exercise

This exercise involves conducting a limited study of a group of primates using the scan sampling technique.

The procedure is as follows:

A. Select a social group of at least 3 animals. It would be best to use an active group of monkeys or strepsirrhines, such as squirrel monkeys, spider monkeys, a species of macaque, or ring-tailed lemurs. Less active species can be used but records may include a lot of resting.

B. Spend sufficient time familiarizing yourself with all of the individual members of the group to enable you to quickly and accurately identify each one (perhaps a review involving exercise 1 would be appropriate).

C. Establish that your ethogram is suitable for the subject group; if it is not, then some modification is warranted.

D. With check-sheets (a sample is provided at the end of this exercise and in the supplementary material), and a watch or stopwatch, (or with a mobile device and an appropriate app), record 40 scans, employing intervals of 15 seconds. Be sure that you include every member of the group in each scan. This will take 10 minutes, then take a few minutes as a break while preparing for the next sample.

One of the most important problems for observers of animal behavior is "observer fatigue" which can rapidly lead to degeneration in the quality of data collected. To prevent this occurrence, regular rest breaks are a necessity.

E. Repeat this sequence 4 times over one hour, i.e., four, 10-minute record sessions that will total up to 160 scans.

F. Calculate the frequency, the rate, and the percentage for each of the behaviors observed for the group as a whole, and then for each age-sex class represented in the group. Finally, prepare your report.

The following sample check-sheet is laid out to handle scan sampling of a group of 5 individuals. Note that the sheet would have to be expanded to handle larger groups.

# Example Check-Sheet for Scan Sampling

Observer: _____ Date: _____

Subject Group: _____ # in group: _____

Start Time: _____ Group Composition: _____

| Time | Subject 1 | Subject 2 | Subject 3 | Subject 4 | Subject 5 |
|------|-----------|-----------|-----------|-----------|-----------|
|      |           |           |           |           |           |
|      |           |           |           |           |           |
|      |           |           |           |           |           |
|      |           |           |           |           |           |
|      |           |           |           |           |           |
|      |           |           |           |           |           |
|      |           |           |           |           |           |
|      |           |           |           |           |           |

# EXERCISE 7

# One/Zero Sampling

One/zero sampling is not often used in primatology because Altmann's (1974) landmark paper strongly discouraged its use. She reasoned that the protocol does not produce data that are either frequency or duration. Your time is better spent on other data collection methods. However, Altmann has noted that if a biologically relevant behavior occurs infrequently enough that a simple presence/absence score is useful, then one/zero sampling might be applicable (J. Altmann, personal communication). Several other researchers accept the usefulness of this procedure and have argued that though the data are neither frequency nor duration, they reflect contributions from both, and consequently, one/zero sampling is a reliable and objective measure of behavior under certain circumstances (Rhine and Flanigan 1978; Rhine and Linville 1980; Rhine and Ender 1983; Rhine et al. 1985; Kraemer 1979). Bernstein (1991) points out in a reasoned comparison that this mixed condition is the core basis of objections to the procedure:

> Critics indicate that the relative contribution of frequencies and duration is a function of the time unit selected. They prefer data on true frequencies or durations as a direct description of animal behavior and reject an abstraction based on a non-specified combination of both. (p. 727)

Bernstein goes on to state, in parallel with Altmann, that a biologically appropriate circumstance might lead to the use of one/zero sampling, when "responses occur in non-independent flurries, where the bout, and not each individual act, is of interest" (Bernstein 1991:727). He suggests that situations such as bouts of play behavior or calculating the probability of receiving aggression during a specific period might be such situations. Kraemer (1979) has also discussed the use of one/zero sampling but suggests that alternatives to one/zero sampling should be used whenever possible. The one benefit to one/zero sampling is that it is easy for multiple observers to arrive at consistent results (i.e., interobserver reliability is high) with this method.

With these caveats in mind, and a quick check back to Figure 2.4 in chapter 2 to remind ourselves of the difference between *sample intervals* and *sample points*, the observational method can be outlined, and the exercise can be set up.

One/zero sampling involves the establishment of a set of observational sample intervals or periods. The intervals may be of any length, though the practical limits are probably 24 hours at the upper end, and 2 seconds at the lower. For the practical purposes of this exercise, and to show the limitations of the method, intervals of 10, 15, 30, or 60 seconds are suggested, and the interval may be explicitly required by the instructor. Timing using a watch, stopwatch, or phone with an audible "beep" when switching between intervals is suggested.

The recording procedure can be done on blank paper, but a prepared check-sheet is more useful. Some apps may be adaptable to one/zero sampling, so consult those listed in chapter 8 (and in the supplementary materials as they are updated) for possibilities. Once observation begins, the observer keeps track of the activities of the subject or subjects and at the end of each sample interval places a tick in the box for the behaviors seen, and a 0 (zero) in the box for the behaviors not seen. No count is made, as the question is "did the behavior occur?" not "how many times did the behavior occur?" An alternative mode of operation is to place the tick mark in the appropriate box as soon as the behavior occurs. This has the advantage of eliminating a memory search (did it or didn't it occur?) at the end of the interval, and in immediately removing that behavior from further consideration.

As with some other methods, it is possible to perform one/zero sampling on a group, or on individuals chosen as subjects one at a time. The results from these two variants are not comparable. The only score or measure that is derived from one/zero sampling is a proportion. The proportion of sample intervals in which the behavior occurred is calculated by simply counting the number of intervals with a tick and dividing by the total number of intervals used for observation. Going beyond this simple calculation is not statistically appropriate.

---

# The Exercise

This exercise involves the conduct of a limited study of a group of primates using the one/zero sampling technique.

The procedure is as follows:

A. Select a social group of at least 4 animals (a minimum of 4 is preferable, though in smaller zoological parks 3 may be the largest number available for any given species). It would be best to use an active group of primates such as squirrel monkeys, ring-tailed lemurs, spider monkeys, or some species of guenon, baboon, or macaque. The instructor will direct you to use either a group or an individual sampling schedule.

B. Spend sufficient time familiarizing yourself with the group to establish that your ethogram is suitable for the subject group; if it is not, then some modification is warranted.

C. With the selection of an appropriate sample interval, 5, 10, 15, 30, or 60 seconds as suggested or required by the instructor, set up a check-sheet for the project.

D. With check-sheets, (a sample is provided below, and is available as supplementary material), and a timer that beeps, record 40 sample intervals. This will take 10 minutes if 15 second intervals are used, forty minutes if 60 second intervals are selected; then take a break while preparing for the next sample.

E. Repeat this sequence 4 times to total up 160 sample intervals.

F. Calculate the proportion for each of the behaviors observed for the group as a whole, or for each age-sex class represented in the group if individual one/zero sampling is to be used. Prepare a data table and a graph showing the variations in proportions found. Finally, prepare your report.

The following sample check-sheet is laid out for one/zero sampling with a maximum ethogram of ten behaviors, and 40 sample intervals. As always, it can also be found with the supplementary material available for this book.

# Example Check-Sheet for One/Zero Sampling

Observer: _____ Date: _____

Subject Group: _____ # in group: _____

| | | | | | | | | | | | |
|---|---|---|---|---|---|---|---|---|---|---|---|
| Start Time: _____ Group Composition: _____ | | | | | | | | | | | |
| Behaviors | | | | | | | | | | | |
| T | | | | | | | | | | | |
| 1 | | | | | | | | | | | |
| 2 | | | | | | | | | | | |
| 3 | | | | | | | | | | | |
| 4 | | | | | | | | | | | |
| 5 | | | | | | | | | | | |
| 6 | | | | | | | | | | | |
| 7 | | | | | | | | | | | |
| 8 | | | | | | | | | | | |
| 9 | | | | | | | | | | | |
| 10 | | | | | | | | | | | |
| 11 | | | | | | | | | | | |
| 12 | | | | | | | | | | | |
| 13 | | | | | | | | | | | |
| 14 | | | | | | | | | | | |
| 15 | | | | | | | | | | | |
| 16 | | | | | | | | | | | |
| 17 | | | | | | | | | | | |
| 18 | | | | | | | | | | | |
| 19 | | | | | | | | | | | |
| 20 | | | | | | | | | | | |
| 21 | | | | | | | | | | | |
| 22 | | | | | | | | | | | |
| 23 | | | | | | | | | | | |
| 24 | | | | | | | | | | | |
| 25 | | | | | | | | | | | |
| 26 | | | | | | | | | | | |
| 27 | | | | | | | | | | | |
| 28 | | | | | | | | | | | |
| 29 | | | | | | | | | | | |
| 30 | | | | | | | | | | | |
| 31 | | | | | | | | | | | |
| 32 | | | | | | | | | | | |
| 33 | | | | | | | | | | | |
| 34 | | | | | | | | | | | |
| 35 | | | | | | | | | | | |
| 36 | | | | | | | | | | | |
| 37 | | | | | | | | | | | |
| 38 | | | | | | | | | | | |
| 39 | | | | | | | | | | | |
| 40 | | | | | | | | | | | |

# EXERCISE 8

# Focal Time Sampling
## State Behavior Interval Sampling Procedure

The procedure called "focal time sampling" is a specialized technique combining some of the features of "focal animal sampling" and "scan sampling." It was introduced by Baulu and Redmond (1978) as an alternative and addition to these two methods of sampling. Focal time sampling is oriented toward the acquisition of state behaviors from a single subject, the "focal subject," at specified intervals over a fixed sample period. This technique is one variation of interval sampling but has the added values of individual identification, and when the interval is short, an approximation to real time. It is also possible and appropriate to add regular, non-behavioral variables into the procedure for ecologically oriented studies. That is, at each interval, the behavior and other variables such as substrate used, tree species occupied, temperature, nearest neighbor, and other variables can be recorded.

In practice, as for focal animal sampling, an observing schedule of focal sample periods has to be pre-established and the sample period is, in each case, devoted to recording only the activities of a single subject plus any select additional variables. It also means that, like scan sampling, the records are only of state behavior, and they are taken at predetermined intervals during the sample period using the same assumption of instantaneous recording as in that technique.

As a consequence, the data records obtained from this method consist of a series of states for the subject taken at intervals, although it is likely that an observer will record data on several aspects of the behavioral state, and, perhaps, environmental factors at each interval. This type of research method requires a well-conceptualized research design and typically will employ a distinctive method of analysis.

## Method and Design Requirements

The method of conduct of focal time sampling is extremely straight forward but is intimately tied to research designs that are oriented toward two particular kinds of analyses—correlations and sequential procedures. As in all observational research, it is necessary to have an appropriate ethogram for use and in this case, the exercise of constructing an observing schedule is a vital prerequisite. The observing procedure during each sample is then simple. The observer maintains visual contact with the selected subject animal, and from the beginning of the sample period records (through the use of check-sheets or with a mobile device) the behavioral state of the subject at fixed intervals.

The intervals and duration of the sample periods are fixed by the observer to be appropriate for the research design objectives. These might vary from 10-minute samples with observations taken at intervals of 10 seconds (yielding 60 records per sample) to 60-minute samples with observations at intervals of 2 minutes (yielding only 30 records per sample), to anything that the observer considers appropriate for the species and research paradigm. Ancillary data may also be collected with each observation, such as the posture of the subject, various orientations to social and/or environmental factors, climatic factors, ecological factors, and such, but the observer must record these as quickly and concisely as possible in order not to violate the assumption that the whole set represents a single slice in time where all the data are acquired at the same instant.

## Research Designs

The research designs employable with focal time sampling are those that are predisposed to the types of statistical analyses mentioned earlier—correlations and sequential statistics. The most appropriate kinds of designs are those where several distinct and independent variables are collected simultaneously with a dependent observed variable for which the independent variables are hypothesized to be causal. As an actual example of a study using this method, a dependent variable—the posture of the subject—was recorded along with a set of independent factors—subject's activity, amount of exposure and orientations to wind and sunlight, height above the ground, the material substrate on which the subject was positioned, and the ambient temperature near the subject. The operating hypotheses were that one or more of the independent factors exerted an influence in inducing the subject to assume various postures that represent changes in the amount of surface area exposed, which in turn indicates aspects of the heat exchange pattern (the results may be viewed in Paterson [1992]). Many variations on the design of research projects are possible, and the student is encouraged to be creative in the formulation and critical in the evaluation of projects.

## Analysis Techniques

The data set from a focal time sampling study may be treated with standard descriptive statistics to yield frequency and relative frequency per sample.

Data can also be converted to yield rates, in particular "bout" rates, and when the intervals between the samples are short enough (it was suggested by Baulu and Redmond [1978] that 10 seconds is usable for this, and other analyses have confirmed its suitability), mean durations per bout and per hour, and percent of time can also be derived. Many of the same table and graph formats for presentation of results are appropriate as for the other methods of observation. Those students with more advanced statistical training may wish to explore techniques of multiple regression, mixed models, Markov chain and lag sequential analysis, or the Lisrel procedures to analyze their data.

## The Exercise

The purpose of this exercise is to provide practice in using the focal time sampling technique (FTS) and preobservation preparatory work in the study of primate behavior. The exercise is to be conducted as follows:

A. Prepare an appropriate ethogram and an observing schedule for the study of a group of 4 or more animals (if possible) using FTS for 10-minute samples with 10-second intervals (60 records per sample). Each animal should be studied several times (the total time involved in the study depends on the number of animals in the group and the number of repeat cycles specified by the instructor). An example of an appropriate study question is to determine if there are age or sex differences found in the behaviors within the study group.

B. Prepare check-sheets for the study—the example for the scan sampling exercise can be utilized, or the version located below (and in the supplementary materials) may be more suitable.

C. Using a timer with a beeper to control the time intervals, conduct the research phase.

D. Perform the analysis of the data and include the calculations of "mean rate per individual" (MRI) and "mean duration per individual" (MDI) as found in chapter 6. These calculations apply to the entire group, or to comparative classes such as male/female, old/young, and so on, but may not be applied to individuals. Another useful calculation would be the "mean duration per bout" (MDB), which is focused on differences in the behaviors of the ethogram, but could also be split along age and sex classes. It is important to remember the difference between a "bout" and a "record" (see chapter 6 for a review). It is also important to provide the total number of scans, the total time involved in the study, and the number of scans per individual in the results.

E. The results may be written up in either a brief or full scientific report as required by the instructor.

# An Advanced Version of the Focal Time Sampling Exercise

For the student with a knowledge and understanding of inferential statistics, in particular of correlation, regression analyses, mixed models, or sequential analysis, a suggested variation on the exercise is as follows.

A. Set up a research design involving the study of a particular aspect of behavior and some structural, locational, climatic, or other easily measured environmental factors. This will involve the construction of an appropriate set of hypotheses about the relationship, and designing the protocol to use FTS in a manner that will provide data to test the hypotheses. If the intention is to focus on sequential analyses, this is irrelevant and only a behavior record is necessary (see Bakeman and Gottman 1997).

B. Conduct the study using at least four subjects in an appropriate social grouping. It is suggested that substantially more time be invested in this project.

C. Employing correlation, regression, mixed models, or sequential statistical procedures (access to a computer with the necessary software is a requirement), analyze the data set for relationships between behavior and the independent variable(s), or for sequential probabilities.

D. Present a scientific report with the appropriate tables and graphs to show support for or rejection of, the hypothesized relationships.

# Example Focal Time Sampling Datasheet

Observer: _____ Date: _____

Subject Group: _____ # in group: _____

| Start Time: _____ Subject Individual: _____ | | | | | | |
|---|---|---|---|---|---|---|
| Time | Behavior | Time | Behavior | Time | Behavior | Remarks |
| 1 | | 1 | | 1 | | |
| 2 | | 2 | | 2 | | |
| 3 | | 3 | | 3 | | |
| 4 | | 4 | | 4 | | |
| 5 | | 5 | | 5 | | |
| 6 | | 6 | | 6 | | |
| 7 | | 7 | | 7 | | |
| 8 | | 8 | | 8 | | |
| 9 | | 9 | | 9 | | |
| 10 | | 10 | | 10 | | |
| 11 | | 11 | | 11 | | |
| 12 | | 12 | | 12 | | |
| 13 | | 13 | | 13 | | |
| 14 | | 14 | | 14 | | |
| 15 | | 15 | | 15 | | |
| 16 | | 16 | | 16 | | |
| 17 | | 17 | | 17 | | |
| 18 | | 18 | | 18 | | |
| 19 | | 19 | | 19 | | |
| 20 | | 20 | | 20 | | |

*(continued)*

# Example Focal Time Sampling Datasheet (cont'd.)

Observer: _____ Date: _____

Subject Group: _____ # in group: _____

| Start Time: _____ Subject Individual: _____ | | | | | | |
|---|---|---|---|---|---|---|
| Time | Behavior | Time | Behavior | Time | Behavior | Remarks |
| 21 | | 21 | | 21 | | |
| 22 | | 22 | | 22 | | |
| 23 | | 23 | | 23 | | |
| 24 | | 24 | | 24 | | |
| 25 | | 25 | | 25 | | |
| 26 | | 26 | | 26 | | |
| 27 | | 27 | | 27 | | |
| 28 | | 28 | | 28 | | |
| 29 | | 29 | | 29 | | |
| 30 | | 30 | | 30 | | |
| 31 | | 31 | | 31 | | |
| 32 | | 32 | | 32 | | |
| 33 | | 33 | | 33 | | |
| 34 | | 34 | | 34 | | |
| 35 | | 35 | | 35 | | |
| 36 | | 36 | | 36 | | |
| 37 | | 37 | | 37 | | |
| 38 | | 38 | | 38 | | |
| 39 | | 39 | | 39 | | |
| 40 | | 40 | | 40 | | |

# EXERCISE 9

# Focal Animal Sampling
## Intensive Study of Behavior

Since the methodological revolution engendered by Altmann's (1974) paper in *Behaviour* (it is suggested that you should have read that paper before reaching this point), the procedure known as "focal animal sampling" has become *the* standard technique for most primate studies. This technique may also be called "continuous sampling" but the procedure remains the same. The essence of focal animal sampling is concentrated attention on a single individual subject for a specific time (the "sample period"), recording everything that the subject does or has done to them, usually with attention paid to the times when behaviors change.

The technique is amenable to the collection of event and state behaviors, and both are generally preferable. In this particular exercise, it is suggested that both event and state behaviors be recorded. The student must, however, separate the two types of data before beginning the analysis. Events happen within state behaviors so this separation is critical; otherwise, the analysis will become invalid and meaningless.

A typical focal animal sampling procedure may be limited to the recording of a specified list of behaviors (the ethogram), which are related to a particular research design/question. But more commonly, the observer will record the totality of behavior initiated by the subject and received by that individual. The key advantage of focal animal sampling over all other techniques is that it allows the observer to collect the maximum amount of information on the behavior of the subjects, and it is the only way to collect data on behavioral sequences without missing anything. The disadvantage is that it can take much more time to collect sufficient data on several individuals since you are only collecting behavior on one individual at a time.

In this sense, the number of individuals and total study time available are important considerations in determining the focal animal sampling period. For example, if you are sampling each individual in a large group of primates (e.g., adult males, adult females, and all immatures), and you have a limited amount of study time available, then shorter focal animal sampling periods (e.g., 10 or 15 minutes) may be appropriate to collect samples from all individuals over different periods and avoid bias. Alternatively, if you are only focused on the adult males in one or two smaller groups of primates, then a longer sampling period (e.g., 30 to 60 or more minutes) may be chosen. It is also advisable to consult the literature as to what focal animal sampling period has typically been employed for your chosen species or research question and follow that if appropriate.

The order of who you sample is also important. This can be accomplished either via a fixed schedule for a short-term study or by randomizing the observation of the subjects in a long-term study (see chapter 2 for a discussion of these aspects). One or the other mechanism must be employed to ensure that each individual in a subject population is sampled equally.

## Important Practical Factors in Focal Sampling Procedures

There are important practical considerations involved in the conduct of a focal animal sampling study. Most significant for the beginning researcher are the following five items:

**Ethogram:** It is important to construct an appropriate ethogram to ensure consistency in the recording of behaviors, with all defined behaviors categorized as either event or state. Students can refer to chapter 3 for more information on defining behaviors in an ethogram. A beginning researcher can consult the library to examine the limited number of published ethograms available. Sometimes, the "Supplementary Materials" section (if available) of published articles provides an ethogram and this is a good place to start looking. If a species-specific ethogram is unavailable, the most appropriate starting point is an ethogram from the most closely related species available.

**Exhaustive categories:** It is most desirable to have exhaustive behavior categories, meaning that the subject is always recorded as being involved in "something" so that a complete time record can be produced. However, behavior categories can be very broad (e.g., "resting" could include sleeping, sitting, or other inactive behaviors) or very fine-grained (e.g., you may have separate behaviors of "sleeping", "sitting", etc.), depending on your research questions.

**Mutually exclusive:** This means that there is no overlap in the behavioral categories (i.e., the subject cannot be recorded as doing two or more activities simultaneously). As such, it may be necessary to generate combined behaviors to record two or more activities that may occur simultaneously (e.g., feeding and sitting in social proximity). For example, an ethogram may have a "feeding" behavior, as well as a "feeding in social proximity" behavior, with the singular "feeding" behavior defined with no other individual in proximity. However, this solution requires extreme care in the analyses stage. One alternative is for a researcher to prioritize recording behaviors that occur simultaneously depending on the research design/question. For example, if your research design is more concerned with feeding behavior than social behavior, then you would prioritize the recording of "feeding" behavior and ignore the social proximity of other individuals. If the researcher does not want to miss recording social proximity, they could combine focal animal sampling with scan samples for near-neighbors (see exercise 12 for combining data collection techniques).

**Recording codes:** A compressed scoring code is a great advantage. It is far faster and simpler to record "DGam4" rather than writing out "directs groom to adult male number four." It is also important to have codes for "out-of-sight," and "indeterminable activity" to achieve an exhaustive record. It is important to record the codes with the behavior definitions in a "codebook," and as part of the ethogram.

**Active (directed) and passive (received) behaviors:** One important factor that has been a stumbling block for beginning observers in the past is the problem of how to deal with the situation in which the focal subject is interacting in some way with another individual or group of individuals. The obvious solution is to create a set of categories in the ethogram that are "active" or "directed" behaviors, and those that are "passive" or "received" behaviors. For example, aggressive behavior should (at the least) be categorized as two distinct behaviors: "directs aggression" and "receives aggression" in the ethogram. The same would apply to friendly behaviors such as grooming—"directs groom" and "receives groom."

---

# The Exercise

The purpose of this exercise is the development of observational skills through the conduct of an in-depth study of the behavior of a single-species group using the technique of focal-animal sampling.

The exercise can be conducted according to the following steps:

A. Select a social group with a minimum of three to four individuals. If the student has been conducting studies on a particular species in previous exercises, now might be the time to broaden the experience envelope and select a new species if available.

B. Ideally, the study should be conducted over more than one day. Construct an observing schedule so that each subject is the focus of the same number of samples. Rotate the sequence so that animals studied late on the first day are looked at earlier on the next, but be careful not to allocate the same subjects to the midday periods.

C. Conduct the sampling using 10, 15, or 20-minute focal samples where a single individual is the subject. Everything that the animal does should be recorded, and the actions of all other individuals not interacting with the focal animal must be ignored to retain a nonbiased sample. Remember to take a short break between each sample to avoid mental and physical fatigue. Records may be taken using the attached sample focal animal datasheet, using a mobile device and associated app, as diary notes on paper, or if care is taken to be concise, then a tape recorder may be used. Be aware that the use of a tape recorder is an invitation to "motor-mouth" and the development of long rambling discourses irrelevant to the study may occur—this leads to long transcription times and can degrade the data quality; however, with certain behavioral sampling situations or species (e.g., fast-moving, brachiating species such as spider monkeys), audio recording of behaviors may be the best option.

D. Once 5 or 10 hours of observation are accumulated, the process of analysis may be started as a check on the validity of hypotheses, design, and variable reliability. The continuance of the study can then go forward with confidence.

E. The analysis of the data must, at a minimum, contain separate tabulations of the frequencies and percentages of event behaviors and of the durations and percentages the state behaviors observed. You are encouraged to make use of as many of the calculations in chapter 6 as are appropriate to the data and the study. These should be tabulated for the group as a whole, as well as for the relevant individual age and sex classes.

F. The final report is to be prepared as a written scientific report in APA format as generally used in primatology journals such as *American Journal of Physical Anthropology, American Journal of Primatology,* or *International Journal of Primatology* (see the discussion of the format of a scientific report in chapter 7 and an example online at waveland.com). Your instructor can choose which APA journal format is preferred, but the important part is to pay attention to the relevant details (e.g., text style, abbreviations, punctuation, spaces), and to be consistent. The report should include the standard Introduction/Methods/Results/Discussion (IMRaD) sections, and be no longer than 12 to 15 typed pages, double-spaced, including tables, graphic presentations, references, and appendices (an actual report to be submitted for publication would generally be longer). The document is expected to reflect not only your direct research results but also the material acquired from the literature. Conclusions should also adequately support or reject similar hypotheses found in the appropriate literature.

G. An ethogram incorporating the compressed code symbols utilized, and an example of a data record should be attached to the report as an appendix.

# An Advanced Version of the Focal Animal Sampling Exercise

An Advanced Version of this exercise would differ only in the expectation that 20 to 30 hours of observation should be conducted. Additionally, such an advanced version may be expected to be a maximum of 20 pages in length to reflect the results of a substantial literature search, and to aspire to the levels of a "publishable report."

# Example Focal Animal Datasheet

Researcher: _____ Date: _____ Time: _____

Subject: _____ Age-Sex: _____ Group: _____

Comments: _____

| Time | Behavior | Other | Comments |
|------|----------|-------|----------|
|      |          |       |          |
|      |          |       |          |
|      |          |       |          |
|      |          |       |          |
|      |          |       |          |
|      |          |       |          |
|      |          |       |          |
|      |          |       |          |
|      |          |       |          |
|      |          |       |          |
|      |          |       |          |
|      |          |       |          |
|      |          |       |          |
|      |          |       |          |
|      |          |       |          |
|      |          |       |          |
|      |          |       |          |
|      |          |       |          |
|      |          |       |          |
|      |          |       |          |
|      |          |       |          |
|      |          |       |          |

# Exercise 10

# All Occurrences Sampling
## Collecting Specified Forms of Behavior

The essence of all occurrences sampling is the direction of attention toward the entire set of subjects for a specific sample period, recording all instances of a limited set of highly visible behaviors. This technique has several restrictive conditions (see below) but when these conditions are met, it can be an effective technique to recover frequencies and synchronization data on event behaviors. The technique is amenable to the collection of event behaviors such as mounts, aggressive episodes, chases, or similar behavior.

The development of an "all occurrences" record is deemed to be possible by Altmann (1974) if the following conditions are present and adhered to:

1. Excellent observing conditions exist. That is, all subject animals must be visible and remain so throughout the sample period.

2. The behaviors are highly visible. That is, the behavior itself must be so obvious that the observer will always see it, and hence all cases will be recorded.

3. The repetition rate for the behavior is slow enough that "all occurrences" can be perceived and recorded.

The duration of the sampling period is not critical but some time control and the recording of observation time is necessary to convert the raw frequencies of occurrences into rates of behavior. Anything from one hour to a day has been successfully employed.

## Important Factors in All Occurrences Sampling

There are some important considerations involved in the conduct of an all occurrences sampling study. Most significant for the beginning researcher are the following items:

**Ethogram:** It is important to have an appropriate ethogram available to ensure consistency in the recording of behaviors, however, only highly visible events need to be defined.

**Mutually exclusive behaviors**: No overlap in the behavioral categories, such that the subjects are recorded as doing two or more activities simultaneously. See exercise 9 for more explanation.

**Recording codes**: A compressed scoring code is of great advantage. It is important to record the codes with the behavior definitions in a "codebook." See exercise 9 for more information.

**Ensured observing conditions**: It is critical to this procedure that all the subjects be visible throughout the observation period. This technique may require the establishment of connections with the zookeepers, and arrangement for the group to be restricted to a single unit of their enclosure. Often this will be unnecessary in the winter months when the group may only have access to an indoor enclosure.

---

# The Exercise

The purpose of this exercise is the development of observational skills through the conduct of a study of the behavior of a single species group employing the technique of all occurrences sampling.

The exercise can be conducted according to the following steps:

A.  Select a social group with a minimum of 3 to 4 individuals. Now may be the time to broaden the experience envelope by selecting a new species.

B.  Check and verify that your ethogram subset, the highly visible dramatic behaviors, such as aggressive episodes, vocalizations, mounting, and such, are clearly defined and appropriate to the study.

C.  Select times or arrange with the zookeepers for times when the group is restricted to a single enclosure.

D.  Conduct the sampling using one-hour long sample periods. Records may be taken using a mobile device with an appropriate app, as diary notes on paper, on a check-sheet constructed for the specific project, or if care is taken to be concise, then an audio recorder may be used . . . but take note of the cautions expressed in exercise 9.

E.  Once 5 hours of observation are accumulated, the process of analysis may be undertaken. Instructors may specify longer or shorter periods and overall study time.

F.  The analysis of the data must, at a minimum, present tabulations of the frequencies and rates of the defined event behaviors observed.

G.  The final report is to be prepared as a written scientific report in the format generally used in primatology journals (see the discussion of the format of a scientific report in chapter 7). The document is expected to reflect not only your direct research results but also the material acquired from reading library sources. Conclusions should also adequately support or reject similar hypotheses found in the appropriate literature.

# EXERCISE 11

# Matched Control Sampling

This technique was originally developed as a method devoted to the study of "reconciliation behavior," a topic first brought to prominence by de Waal and van Roosmalen (1979); however, matched control sampling can be applied more widely and it works well in certain situations to establish a baseline of interaction between individuals. Below, we will discuss matched control sampling in the context of studying reconciliation, but we will also provide examples of how this sampling procedure may be useful in other contexts.

Reconciliation was a hot topic in primatology during the late 1980s and 1990s, and thus is the focus of a large body of literature. The concept is based on the premise that for a social group of primates to maintain its existence, there must be mechanisms to reestablish friendly relations after a conflict situation has developed. This implies that some behaviors or interactions serve to reduce anxiety to baseline levels and these can be categorized as affinitive behaviors showing social attraction between the participants. For clarity, "affinitive behaviors" are typically defined as behaviors that show a "liking" or "attraction" to another individual, such as approaches, proximity, or affiliation.

> Affinitive contact between former opponents soon after a conflict has been demonstrated in a growing number of primate species. Several recent studies show that such contact reduces the probability of future conflicts, allows the recipient of aggression to reduce its anxiety, and restores tolerance between former opponents. Hence, these contacts can be termed reconciliation. (Kappeler and van Schaik 1992: 51)

However, reconciliation has been operationally defined using different criteria in different species by different observers, and no single definition is universally recognized. "Functional reconciliation," on the other hand, can be clearly defined as "behavior that restores a dyadic social relationship" (Cords 1993:255). Cords goes on to show that for long-tailed macaques (*Macaca fascicularis*) the operational reconciliation can be defined as:

> (i) first post-conflict nonaggressive encounters between former opponents, including mere proximity, (ii) occurring after a conflict sooner than expecta-

tions based on the baseline interaction rate measured (once) for the same dyad at about the same time, (iii) regardless of which opponent initiates the encounter. (Cords 1993:264)

Cords sees the above as agreeing closely with the functional definition of reconciliation. It must generally be conceded that there will be differing behaviors employed as reconciliation in different species, and not all species display more than a minimal frequency of the phenomenon. In most studies of reconciliation, the first task has normally been to establish that it exists. It is only then that the observer can proceed to study it.

The technique of "matched control" sampling is distinctive in that it incorporates a control sample that is tested against another sample. In reconciliation studies, this test sample is a "Post-Conflict" period, triggered by the observation of an aggressive conflict (but in theory any behavior could be examined with this method). Hence, the frequently encountered reference in the literature to "PC/MC," or post-conflict, matched control study paradigm.

The pattern for MC sampling is as follows: A "trigger behavior" is established as the signal to begin a sample observation. In reconciliation studies, this is usually an aggressive conflict between two individuals. At this point, the observer begins a focal animal sample on *one* of the combatants, usually between 10 and 20 minutes long. The choice of which animal is the focal animal can be random, perhaps decided at the moment by the flip of a coin or by a pre-established protocol (e.g., "A" has more samples recorded than "B," select B as focal next time there is a conflict between A and B), or an observing rule (e.g., always observe the aggressor in a conflict).

The second component—the "matched control"—is a second focal animal sample of the same length conducted on the same subject but 24 hours later, starting at approximately the same time as the post-conflict sample began. Many researchers have added specific criteria regulating the start of the MC sample. Some have employed a "spatial criterion," requiring the two subjects to be within a specific distance of each other, or in the same subgrouping. These criteria may have greater validity in free-ranging animals than in captive groups (Kappeler and van Schaik 1992). However, the most common criteria have been limited to the timing and the absence of agonism between the subject pair before the MC sample's start.

The method of observation is simple, as regular focal animal sample records are collected; however, the difficulties come with the analysis of the data. As a result, two techniques have been developed: one where there is a specific comparison made between the PC sample and the corresponding MC sample; and a second where a baseline level of interaction and proximity is based on aggregate MC samples (Kappeler and van Schaik 1992). Silk (1997) has further criticized the MC methodology by pointing out that:

If conflict damages social relationships and these effects persist over time, . . . then it seems inappropriate to conduct the matched control observation on the day after conflict has occurred. . . . A better alternative would be to collect baseline data that can be retrospectively matched with post-conflict observations. (p. 267)

This critique is valid for reconciliation studies but the MC protocol has also been employed in other types of studies. For instance, it can be used as a way to compare behavior occurrence after experimental manipulation, like a vocalization playback, versus during baseline observations (e.g., Engh et al. 2006); or as a way to compare energy expenditure (i.e., travel time and duration) in different contexts (e.g., Amsler 2010); or to account for proximity between interactants that may be exchanging behaviors as commodities (e.g., Gumert 2007), among other examples.

As can be seen, care and caution must be exercised in any matched control study. The exercise will focus on the main variants of MC analyses and not require the construction of baseline data collection. Even though the example is on post-conflict behavior, similar considerations regarding the analysis of MC data would need to be assessed for other research questions where this method is used.

# Analysis of MC sampling

The following discussion of analytical approaches to PC/MC data is based on figure two and its caption in Kappeler and van Schaik (1992). Diagram A presents the basic comparative framework for PC-MC studies. Diagram B shows the first analytical procedure.

The *conciliatory tendency method* relies only on the PC data and presents results as a "reconciliation" (represented by the black dot in Diagram B) if affinitive behavior occurs at all. The only quantitative analysis possible is to measure the time between conflict and reconciliation, and then present an average for group or age-sex classes. Decisions about whether or not the conflict is resolved in this method are dependent on the length of the sampling period.

Diagram C presents the *conservative reconciliation method*, which only considers a conflict to be resolved if affinitive behavior occurs in the PC sample but *not* in the MC sample. This technique can produce false-negative evaluations if affinitive behavior occurs in the MC sample (Kappeler and van Schaik 1992).

In Diagram D, the *attracted pairs method* is diagrammed. All conflicts that are followed by an affinitive interaction are categorized as "reconciled" if the affinitive behavior occurs earlier in the PC sample than in the MC sample, and as "unreconciled" if later than in the MC. This technique also has some limitations derived from probability assumptions and produces the occasional false positive and false negative evaluations.

The *n-minute* or *time rule* method shown in Diagram E applies a rule derived from a larger set of control samples. A large number of sample periods are set up as control periods and the rates that affinitive interactions occur are used to decide the time rule. This is beyond the requirements of the exercise, and for practical application, we suggest that a "two-minute rule" be used for this analysis. This means that if the affinitive behavior occurs earlier than two minutes after the conflict, the conflict is categorized as "reconciled," if later in the sample, it results in categorization of "unreconciled."

The final component in this analysis chain is then a calculation of the percentage or proportion of reconciled versus unreconciled conflicts. As always this may be broken down by age-sex class, dyads, or even to individual levels.

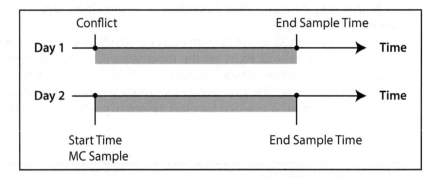

**Diagram A**   Basic comparative framework for PC/MC studies

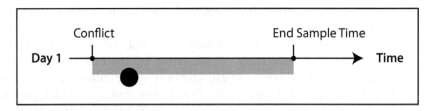

**Diagram B**   Conciliatory tendency method

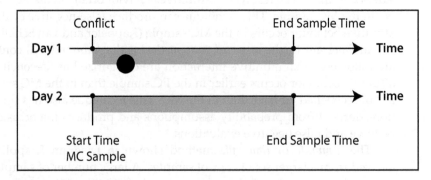

**Diagram C**   Conservative reconciliation method

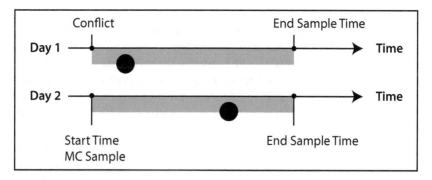

**Diagram D**  Attracted pairs method

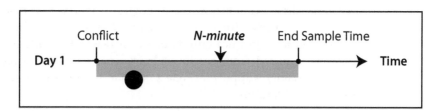

**Diagram E**  N-minute or time rule method

# The Exercise

The purpose of this exercise is the conduct of a study of the behavior of a single species group employing the technique of post-conflict, matched-control sampling. The exercise can be conducted according to the following steps:

A. Select a social group with a minimum of 3–4 individuals. The larger the group is, the more opportunities exist for the study to obtain adequate data.

B. Check and verify that your ethogram is clearly defined and appropriate to the study. You must know what conflict looks like in the species and what behaviors might be defined as affinitive to potentially serve the purpose of reconciliation.

C. Conduct the sampling by watching the study group until a conflict takes place. Immediately note the time and begin a focal animal sample on one of the subjects involved (this individual must be identified). Records may be taken using a mobile device and appropriate app, as diary notes on paper, or if care is taken to be concise, then an audio recorder may be used, but take note of the cautions expressed in exercise 9.

D. On the following day, continue with informal watching of the study group, but pay attention to the individuals involved in the interaction of the previous day during the 15 minutes before the time designated for the start of the MC sample. If conflict does not reoccur, the MC sample may proceed to be recorded. However, if a conflict takes place during this period, the MC should be postponed until the following day (note that this may result in a chain of postponements, and is one of the factors that Silk [1997] criticizes).

E. The analysis of the data must present tabulations of the number of conflicts and reconciliations observed. It should also make use of the conciliatory tendency, conservative reconciliation, attracted pairs, and n-minute rules to compare the different analysis methods.

F. The final report is to be prepared as a written scientific report in the format generally used in major primatology journals (see the discussion of the format of a scientific report in chapter 7 and online). The document is expected to reflect not only your direct research results but also the material acquired from reading library sources. Conclusions should also adequately support or reject similar hypotheses found in the appropriate literature.

# EXERCISE 12

# Combining Data Collection Techniques

When designing any research project, it is important to ensure that you are collecting all the data you need to answer your research question(s). This means obtaining unbiased data on your variables of interest and also on any variables that may be confounding and need to be controlled. For long research projects, such as those that may be undertaken in graduate school, it may also be the case that certain types of data have to be collected routinely throughout the study (e.g., over one year, so that each season is represented in each type of data). Functionally, this leads to the concurrent collection of data using several different data collection techniques. Below, we provide some guidance on maximizing your results.

## Alternating Data Collection Methods

Since different data collection techniques allow different kinds of analysis or are considered ideal for answering certain questions, it is likely that, at times, you will want to employ two or more. As an example, during her PhD research, Julie Teichroeb collected 10-minute focal animal samples on individual ursine colobus during full-day follows. In between focal samples, every 30 minutes, a scan was conducted at the group level to collect information on all the trees occupied and the location of the group's approximate center of mass. Additionally, if an intergroup encounter began, all occurrence data on aggressive behaviors were collected as long as the groups were within 50 m of one another. This was all concurrent with monthly group censuses to note membership, opportunistic collection of fecal samples for hormone and parasite analyses, recording of roar choruses in the early morning, biweekly phenology surveys, ecological plots, as well as recording rainfall and temperature once a day from gauges at the research station. You can see why scheduling becomes important in a large research project. All of these data created a thorough record of colobus behavior and environmental conditions for the duration of the project that yielded several publications.

Melin et al. (2018) detail how different data collection techniques are used together in the long-term project on white-faced capuchin (*Cebus capucinus*) life histories in Santa Rosa National Park, Costa Rica. They point out a notable benefit of alternating between scan sampling and focal animal sampling: If scan sampling is used to collect time budget data in an unbiased way, then focal animal sampling can be used concurrently in a more flexible manner. Specifically, focal samples can be targeted to certain behaviors. Also, focal animal samples in this scenario do not have to be as bound by a strict predetermined schedule among individuals or a strict out-of-sight rule. Thus, focal samples are biased, but for a reason. You cannot extract information such as how often or for how long individuals perform a certain behavior from these data; however, you can get detailed sequences of events targeting individuals involved in certain behavior. At Santa Rosa, this strategy allowed researchers to collect intensive data on food investigation sequences and intake rates (Melin et al. 2018).

## Integrating Data Collection Methods

The strategy detailed above, collecting several data types and alternating between different data collection methods, is powerful and used by most field primatologists. Though less flexible, it is also possible, to integrate techniques to collect different types of data on the same animal at the same time by embedding scan samples within focal animal samples.

As an example, you may want to record all the neighbors within 5 m of your focal animal during a focal animal sample. However, taking your eyes off of your subject every time the compliment of neighbors shifts makes it difficult to ensure that you are not losing any behaviors performed by or directed toward your focal animal. One way around this issue is to design your data collection technique to include scan samples embedded within your focal animal samples. Therefore, if your focal animal sample is 10 minutes long, you could conduct a scan on the neighbors within five meters of your subject every minute, or every two minutes. This would give you data on the neighbors around your subject with less risk of losing important details on the behaviors of your focal individual.

Integration of scans within focal animal samples can be done for any data that could change during the focal sample time but are difficult to record continuously, such as height in the canopy, tree species occupied, tree ID code, canopy cover around the animal, substrate used, body positioning, proximity, temperature, wind speed, and potentially others. Proficiency will come with practice, but it may also be useful to incorporate research assistants to aid in integrated data collection methods where possible.

# Important Practical Considerations

The exercise below involves integrating scan sampling and focal animal sampling. It should not be undertaken until after the student has completed exercises 6 and 9, and is sufficiently familiar with these two data collection techniques on their own. As with any study using focal animal sampling, the student must ensure that they have:

1. an appropriate **ethogram**, including event and state behaviors where state behaviors are mutually exclusive and there are exhaustive categories, so that the subject is always recorded as doing something;

2. compressed **recording codes**, including one for "out-of-sight" and ways to indicate directed and received behaviors.

# The Exercise

The purpose of this exercise is the development of observational skills by conducting a project that combines the data collection techniques of focal animal sampling and scan sampling.

The exercise can be conducted according to the following steps:

A. Select a social group with a minimum of 3 to 4 individuals. It is best to use a species or social group that you are familiar with since efficiently combining data collection techniques is a skill that requires practice.

B. Considering the time available and the scope of the project, construct an observing schedule so that each subject is the focus of the same number of samples. If the project is going to be conducted over multiple days, rotate the sequence so that animals studied late on the first day are looked at earlier on the next, but be careful not to allocate the same subjects to the midday periods.

C. Conduct the sampling using 10- or 20-minute focal samples in which a single individual is the subject. Every two minutes, record the age-sex class or identity of the neighbors within 5 m of the focal animal in four distance categories: 0 m (body contact), <1 m, 1–3 m, 3–5 m. To do this, it will be helpful to have a digital watch or timer set to beep every 2 minutes. Remember to take a short break between each sample to avoid mental and physical fatigue. For 10-minute focal animal samples, records may be taken using the datasheet on the next page. Alternatively, a mobile device and associated app, diary, or recording device may be used.

D. The analysis of the data must, at a minimum, contain separate tabulations of the frequencies and percentages of event behaviors and the durations and percentages of the state behaviors observed in your focal samples. As well, the scans on the proximity of neighbors can be analyzed using an appropriate association index, as discussed in chapter 4 and exercise 14. If enough data are collected, the student may even try to construct a social network based on proximity.

E.  The detail and length of the final report can be dictated by your instructor. Be sure to include your ethogram incorporating the compressed code symbols utilized, and an example of a data record as an appendix.

# Example Datasheet for Combining Methods

Researcher: _____ Date: _____ Time: _____

Subject: _____ Age-Sex: _____ Group: _____

Comments: _____

| Time | Behavior | Other | Comments |
|------|----------|-------|----------|
|      |          |       |          |
|      |          |       |          |
|      |          |       |          |
|      |          |       |          |
|      |          |       |          |
|      |          |       |          |
|      |          |       |          |
|      |          |       |          |
|      |          |       |          |
|      |          |       |          |
|      |          |       |          |
|      |          |       |          |
|      |          |       |          |
|      |          |       |          |
|      |          |       |          |
|      |          |       |          |
|      |          |       |          |

**Scan Samples**

| Time | 0 m | <1 m | 1–3 m | 3–5 m |
|------|-----|------|-------|-------|
| 2    |     |      |       |       |
| 4    |     |      |       |       |
| 6    |     |      |       |       |
| 8    |     |      |       |       |
| 10   |     |      |       |       |

# Testing and Analysis
## Tools for Understanding Behavior

# EXERCISE 13

# Interobserver Reliability Testing
## Do Two People See the Same Things?

Any science that depends on human perception as the main source of data has a large problem to resolve. The deficiencies of human perception and individual bias place the reliability of all research in primatology (and by extension, all other observational sciences) into question. Fortunately, awareness of these deficiencies is, in itself, half of the solution to the problem. If one is aware of the problem, then steps to either correct or make allowances for it can be taken and objective evaluations can be made. The correction of perceptual biases is an internal process unique to each observer; how then can anyone place any degree of confidence in the results that someone else has produced? The solution lies in the realm of reliability testing.

## Reliability Testing or Observer Agreement?

Bakeman and Gottman (1997) point out that there is some disagreement about the meanings of *observer agreement* versus *observer reliability*. Johnson and Bolstad (1973) argue that "agreement" is a general term describing the extent to which two observers agree with each other. "Reliability" is more restrictive and derived from psychometrics where it is used to demonstrate how accurate a measure is. Reliability for an observer can only be assessed against a standard protocol.

The reliability of results can be dramatically improved through the adoption of appropriate methods of data collection. Achieving a high level of competence in observation is the object of these exercises. Control of methodology and utilization of realistic research design can significantly improve the quality of data that an individual observer collects, but we must remain aware that all observations are still filtered through a human brain—a brain that may or may not see things in the same way as other brains. The solution to this dilemma has been available for some time in what is referred to as "interobserver reliability testing." The process is critical when conducting behavioral data collection with more than one observer; however, it is also used to ensure that single observers do not drift in their perceptions and definitions of behaviors throughout their project.

It ought to be apparent that the simplest way to test one's observational reliability is to make a concurrent check to find out if what one observer records as behavior "A" is the same as what another observer records. Over the years, this has evolved into a regularly used coefficient of reliability, $R$, which is a proportional value that equals 1.00 when the two observers are in perfect agreement.

$$R = \frac{s}{\left[\dfrac{t}{2}\right]}$$

In the equation, $R$ is the coefficient of reliability, $s$ is the number of same behavior records scored by two observers, and $t$ is the total number of behaviors collected by the observer pair.

It is generally considered that a value of $R = 0.90$ or better is needed for the results of two observers to be comparable in any useful way (Martin and Bateson 2007), though some consider an $R$-value of 0.98 or higher to be the standard of acceptability. $R$ is tested and determined in the following manner/s:

1. Two observers who are to check their reliability set up to make a "test observation for reliability." This is done by the two workers independently observing the *same subject* at the *same time* for the *same observational period*.

2. Typically, the two observers will independently record continuous data using focal animal sampling for a fixed period (usually 10 or 15 minutes is sufficient) on the same subject. Alternatively, or to facilitate a quick test, focal time sampling may be used if only state behaviors are to be validated.

   A critical condition for reliability testing is that during the test, there must be no communication between the observers, although they should be relatively close together to have similar angles of view.

3. At the end of the test, the two compare their records side by side and calculate their coefficient of reliability, or $R$-value.

4. $R$ can be calculated by using the above formula and multiplied by 100 to obtain a percentage agreement value instead of a proportion. An alternate formula that may be easier to calculate uses the number of "agreements" ($N_a$) and the number of "disagreements" ($N_d$) as in the following formula, which can also be multiplied by 100 to obtain a percentage agreement:

$$R = \frac{N_a}{N_a + N_d}$$

5. As an example, where two observers recorded 139 total behaviors, Observer One with 70 records, and Observer Two with 69 records of which 66 are the same as Observer One's, the calculation is as follows:

$$s = 66 \qquad t = 139$$

$$R = \frac{s}{\left[\dfrac{t}{2}\right]}$$

$$R = 0.9496$$

and the percentage agreement can be rounded off to 95%.

In the alternate calculation, $Na$ is 66, and $Nd$ is 4 (three direct coding differences and one behavior missed by Observer Two); therefore, the value calculates to 0.9428 for a percentage of agreement of 94%. The two formulae will give slightly different results.

6. While the resulting 94 to 95% agreement falls within the baseline level of acceptance (and is considered better than average for beginners), it is not very good for professional observers. In this case, the two observers would proceed to compare their behavioral categorizations and discuss what it was that they saw differently. The reasons for the discrepancies may be immediately apparent to the two observers, or it may take some time to find them. In this example, since the counts of behaviors seen by each observer differ (70 versus 69) by one, it is possible that Observer Two was inattentive and simply missed a behavior change. On the other hand, the situation might be more complicated, with Observer One making finer distinctions within a certain behavior set, which Observer Two considers to be all the same thing, yielding the three items coded differently between their records. In any case, the "test" is repeated and discussed until a satisfactory $R$ score is achieved.

In many team-based research projects, reliability testing is built into the schedule so that each observer of a team is tested against every other as a matter of course at regular points throughout the study. This could be weekly, biweekly, monthly, or at some other interval depending on the length of the study and number of observers. For more observers (or a greater rotation of observers), reliability testing should be scheduled more often. This serves the important function of maintaining behavioral category agreement among all the members of the observing team over what may be a lengthy study period, assuring that the behavioral categories remain the same from beginning to end, and from observer to observer. Such procedures fall into the category of true "reliability testing" and have the added advantage that seasoned observers can leave and new ones can be incorporated into the study team without the loss of data or the distortion of behavioral categories.

For the individual observer conducting a long-term project, the matter of reliability testing is not one that can be sloughed off and ignored. Instead, it is an activity that can prove to be vitally important to the validity of the entire data set. The problem for such an individual researcher is that there is no one to test against, and, hence, they must resort to a form of self-testing, one that has significant commonality with the "pre-test/post-test" paradigm used in psychology and medicine. Under this self-testing procedure, the observer conducts a sample test at the beginning of the study (but after the initial test and revisions of design have been completed) and prepares a formal ethogram description of the behaviors. Periodically thereafter, the observer takes sample tests for comparison to the original record, and the ethogram. A periodic examination of the ethogram may help to maintain consistency. Another alternative, where video equipment is available, is for the observer to prepare a 10- or 20-minute live record, and then to periodically play the tape and record data from it as if seeing it for the first time. The observer can then compare new with past records and calculate the $R$-value between the samples. Utilization of one or the other of these variations is an aid to maintaining consistency in the quality of data.

## The Exercise

The purpose of this exercise is to evaluate the interobserver agreement between two observers.

A. Two observers will set up an ethogram, or preferably use an established ethogram set of behaviors, and agree to conduct an observational test on an appropriately active species, using either focal time sampling (10-minute sample period with 10-second intervals = 60 observations is suggested) or focal animal sampling for 10 minutes. It is important to choose an active species or times when animals are more active so that the reliability of observation in behavior changes can be tested. If animals are inactive there is little point to conducting the test.

B. The test should be conducted twice, with an evaluation stage in between each test to correct perceptual errors. This will be relatively easy if focal time sampling is being used and consequently, the records may be matched observation by observation to locate disagreements. The process will be slightly more complex if using focal animal sampling since event behaviors may also be recorded but the derivation of a behavioral sequence is straightforward.

C. The two observers jointly discuss the behavior sequences recorded and note the "omissions" and "perceptual variations" in the data. Note that if you are comparing lists on a side-by-side basis and one observer has missed a behavior, then the sequence will be misaligned from that point. The omission should be identified and the alignment corrected before proceeding to calculate the $R$-value.

D. The coefficient **R** is to be calculated after each stage and recorded. If the two observers are in perfect accord after the first test (that is, **R** = 1.0), the two observers may choose to conduct the second test as focal animal sampling over a 20-minute sample to extend their self-evaluation.

E. Finally, a report may be prepared in the form required by the instructor.

---

# An Advanced Version of the Interobserver Reliability Testing Exercise With Cohen's Kappa Calculation

Bakeman and Gottman (1997) review several criticisms of the use of agreement percentages as an estimate of observer reliability. They point out that there is no rational basis for considering a percentage agreement value in the 90+ percent range to be "good." They also note that the number of codes used can influence the percentage agreement, and consequently comparability is lost between studies. The two authors go on to provide a most telling argument against its use:

> Given a particular coding scheme and a particular recording strategy, some agreement would occur just by chance alone, even with blindfolded observers, and agreement percentage scores do not correct for this. (Bakeman and Gottman 1997:61)

What is the solution to these defects? The authors provide a thorough examination of the utility and validity of Cohen's *kappa* as applied to observer agreement. The *kappa* statistic corrects for chance agreement but requires the generation of an "agreement" or "confusion" table that shows graphically where similar and dissimilar decisions by two observers occur.

Figure 13E.1 demonstrates the cases where agreement and disagreement between two observers took place in a test example. Disagreements occurred in each behavior category but a percentage agreement value **R** of 87% can still be obtained. With these data in hand, it is possible to calculate the value of *kappa*. We will only deal with the basic calculation, and if correction factors are needed the reader is referred to the detailed discussion in chapter 4 of Bakeman and Gottman (1997). The basic kappa formula is:

$$\kappa = \frac{P_{\text{obs}} - P_{\text{exp}}}{1 - P_{\text{exp}}}$$

Two additional calculations are needed to derive the value of *kappa* and they can be calculated from the confusion table values. $P_{obs}$ is the observed proportion of agreement and is calculated by summing the values in the diagonal and dividing by the total number of observations. In the example table above, this is $(7 + 24 + 17 + 25 + 14)/100$, so $P_{obs} = 0.87$. Similarly, the value of $P_{exp}$ is the proportion that is expected by chance and is calculated by summing

|  | Second Observer | | | | | |
|---|---|---|---|---|---|---|
|  | Social | Feed | Move | Rest | Other | Totals |
| Social | 7 | 0 | 1 | 0 | 0 | 8 |
| Feed | 1 | 24 | 0 | 0 | 0 | 25 |
| Move | 1 | 1 | 17 | 2 | 2 | 23 |
| Rest | 0 | 0 | 3 | 25 | 1 | 29 |
| Other | 0 | 0 | 0 | 1 | 14 | 15 |
| Totals | 9 | 25 | 21 | 28 | 17 | 100 |

(First Observer labels the rows.)

**Figure 13E.1** "Agreement" or "confusion" matrix table (modified from Bakeman and Gottman [1997:62]). Values on the diagonal indicate agreement and off-diagonal values show the number of cases of disagreement for each of the five categories of behavior used in the test study.

the products of the marginals. The total for row 1 is multiplied by the total for column 1, added to the product of row 2 by column 2, added to the product of row 3 by column 3, and so on until the entire matrix is used, then this value is divided by the square of the number of observations.

$$\text{Thus } P_{exp} = \frac{(9 \times 8) + (25 \times 25) + (21 \times 23) + (28 \times 29) + (17 \times 15)}{100 \times 100}$$
$$= 0.2247$$

$$\text{Therefore } \kappa = \frac{0.87 - 0.2247}{1 - 0.2247}$$

$$= 0.8323 \text{ (after rounding)}$$

One of the advantages of using *kappa* is that the distribution is known and a *kappa* value can be tested for significance; however, this is beyond the needs or expectations of this workbook, and the reader is again referred to chapter 4 of Bakeman and Gottman (1997).

The advanced exercise is the same as the simpler version except that the calculation of *kappa* is required. The accompanying form may be used to work through both versions of this exercise.

# Reliability Testing: 1

Name: _____ Partner Name: _____

I.D.#: _____ I.D.#: _____

Species/Group Observed: _____

Test Date: _____ Time: _____

| OBSERVER ONE CODES | OBSERVER TWO CODES |
|---|---|
| | |
| CALCULATION OF *R or kappa* | PERCENTAGE AGREEMENT |
| | |

# Reliability Testing: 2

Name: _____ Partner Name: _____

I.D.#: _____ I.D.#: _____

Species/Group Observed: _____

Test Date: _____ Time: _____

| REPORTER'S CODES | PARTNER'S CODES |
|---|---|
| | |
| CALCULATION OF *R or kappa* | PERCENTAGE AGREEMENT |
| | |

# EXERCISE 14

# Measures of Association

As described in chapter 4, interaction matrices and sociograms serve as visual tools of analyses and as presentation devices. An interaction matrix or a sociogram can assist during the analysis phase, and can also be employed as the primary means of presenting the results of matrix analysis. Interaction rates and indices of association take those data one step further in that they analyze the underlying relationships of dyads within a group relative to other dyads. Refer to chapter 4 for more information on each of these measures of association before undertaking the following exercises.

---

## The Exercises

### Matrices and Sociograms

The purpose of this exercise is to develop some skill and facility in generating analytic structures (matrices and sociograms). Therefore, for the first part of this exercise, both a matrix and a sociogram are to be constructed and presented in final form. It is most appropriate for this exercise to make use of the data collected by focal animal sampling, and consequently, it may be appropriate to employ this exercise in conjunction with one of the methodology training exercises. In that case, the matrices and sociograms generated would be included as part of the "presentation of results" section of the report. If this exercise is conducted separately, it could be done on either data collected by the student specifically for this purpose (all occurrences sampling might be appropriately used), or it could be done on a prepared data set provided to the student. Whatever source data are used, the final product should be a standard scientific report.

### Proximity (or Nearest Neighbor) Study Design and Data Analyses

In this expanded exercise, students go through the scientific process and hone their skills in collecting and analyzing association data.

A. The first step is to devise a research question that will be answerable through the data collected in a proximity study.

B. Next, design the data collection protocol by setting up the appropriate variables, measurements, and analytical mechanisms that would be used in the conduct of such a study. At this point, the types of analyses you want to perform later must be considered. Scan samples for interindividual proximity can give you data on association frequency rates but if you are also interested in durations and who maintains proximity to whom, focal animal sampling must be done so that time in each behavior and approaches and leaves can be recorded.

C. Data can then be collected on the basis of this study design, or the instructor may provide a data set for analyses.

D. Based on data collected or provided, calculate interaction rates for all dyads within your study group. The instructor can help to determine units of effort based on the time available to conduct the observations. Interaction rates can be symmetric or asymmetric, so this exercise will involve symmetric interactions based on proximity. If your data are appropriate, you can also calculate asymmetric associations such as the maintenance of proximity (i.e., approaches and leaves) for your dyads. In addition, calculate an association index using the simple ratio index provided your assumptions hold (see Whitehead 2008:98); otherwise, a half- or twice-weight index would likely be appropriate. With analyses complete, write a standard scientific report on your findings.

# EXERCISE 15

# A Phenological Transect Survey
## What Plants Are in Which Phases
## of Their Cycles in the Area?

Similar in pattern to a line transect survey of populations is a phenological transect survey, though the methods and objectives differ significantly. Vegetation cyclicity, the pattern of change in leaf and reproductive components, is a major force influencing many of the population dynamic and demographic factors in a primate society and the animal community as a whole. Consequently, these cyclical patterns are of interest to primatologists. Vegetation cycles in the form of "stable" and "fluctuating" patterns are often labeled as "predictable" and "unpredictable" and used to evaluate habitat type (Colwell 1974; Stearns 1981). The importance of the plant periodicity to the ecological relationships of the primates cannot be overstated. Frankie et al. (1974) make the following statement that is perfectly applicable to primate research:

> Major patterns of leaf flushing are informative since numerous phytophagous organisms must be synchronized in their life cycles with the succulent leaf resources that become available during peak periods of leafing. . . . Conversely, major periods of leaf fall must be important to the dynamics of litter organisms that occur in both forests.
>
> Many phenological patterns observed . . . fit well with the seasonal cycle of climatic conditions. However, some patterns may be importantly influenced by biotic as well as by abiotic factors. (p. 906)

These patterns of periodicity in leaf production and leaf fall can be seen to have a straightforward relationship to the diet available to leaf consuming species whether they are specialists on new or old leaves, but they are equally important to species that feed on insects. The insect population will largely fall into the "numerous phytophagous organisms" category used above and their availability will be dependent on the leaf flush. Flowering and fruiting cycles can be viewed in the same fashion.

Phenology then is the study of the cyclic patterns of leafing, flowering, and fruiting. A detailed sequence of phenophases in leaf and reproductive components can be set up as follows, with recording codes L0 to L11 and R0 to R16, though this is a much finer set of distinctions than may be generally in use:

| Leaf | | Reproductives | |
|------|------|------|------|
| L0 | dormant | R0 | dormant |
| L1 | initial bud | R1 | initial bud |
| L2 | developing bud | R2 | developing bud |
| L3 | mature bud | R3 | mature bud |
| L4 | initial leaf | R4 | initial flower |
| L5 | new leaf | R5 | juvenile flower |
| L6 | juvenile leaf | R6 | mature flower |
| L7 | full new leaf | R7 | open flower |
| L8 | mature leaf | R8 | pollinated flower |
| L9 | old leaf | R9 | petals discarded |
| L10 | degenerate leaf | R10 | small immature fruit (seed set) |
| L11 | discarded leaf | R11 | larger juvenile fruit |
| | | R12 | full-sized immature fruit |
| | | R13 | staged ripening of fruit—1, 2, 3, 4 |
| | | R14 | fully ripe fruit |
| | | R15 | degenerate fruit |
| | | R16 | discarded fruit |

It is also possible to make the record even more fine-grained by dividing each tree into quadrants using the cardinal directions, and recording phenophases for each of the quadrants, then averaging them for the tree's final score. However, because most phenology surveys are done on a routine basis and many trees are monitored, most botanical studies employ a limited set of phenophase categories such as: "flower buds, flowers, immature fruits, and mature fruits" (de Lampe et al. 1992) to save time. A common pattern in primatological studies is to measure the young and mature availability of each plant part on a scale of 0–4, where each number represents a proportion of what is on the plant. Where, 0 = 0% and thus that plant part is not present, 1 = 1–25%, 2 = 26–50%, 3 = 51–75%, and 4 = 76–100%. Typically, each category for each plant part, if it is present, will equal 4. An example is demonstrated in Table 15E.1 below.

As you can see in Table 15E.1, for each plant part that is present, the numbers for young and mature items equal 4, or 100%, so the proportions present are taken into consideration. So, for example, on the crown of the *Albizia zygia* tree, of all leaves present, there are about 75% mature leaves and 25% young leaves; of the seed pods present, about 25% are unripe and 75% are ripe; and no flowers were seen. Zeros are used when no items from that particular plant part are present on the crown of the tree. The column is left blank if that species does not produce that particular type of plant part. For instance, *Ficus* species do not produce flowers in the traditional sense because "blossoms" are hidden from view in a receptacle, called a "syconium," which eventually becomes the fig and it just looks like an immature fruit. When using this type of method, some researchers separate seeds from fleshy fruits for ease of analysis later since usually trees either produce one or the other. It is a matter of preference whether the researcher wants these to be combined or separated.

This method works well but one issue with it is that it does not provide any indication of the quantity or number (i.e., the fullness of the canopy) of each plant part available. For example, because the numbers from each plant part must equal 0 or 4, a plant listed with 75% young leaves and 25% mature leaves might have a crown that is full of leaves or a relatively bare crown with few leaves. The numbers presented do not give you this information. To include these data, researchers may add a column for each plant part for relative quantity. Actual estimates of the number of items present can be included or it can just be noted whether the crown is full, partially full, or relatively bare. Estimates of fruit production or the remaining standing crop of certain plant parts have been done in different ways. Normally it would be impossible to perform a complete count, but by visually gridding the crown into a dozen or more sectors and counting two or preferably three of these, it is possible to produce a reasonably close estimate of the amount of fruit, or other parts of interest, present at one point in time. Sample record sheets for a basic and a fine-grain phenological survey are attached at the end of this exercise and are available with the supplementary material for the book.

An alternative method of phenological data collection, presented in Table 15E.2, can be used that takes the number of items into account. In this method, the numbers for each plant part do not need to equal 4 if the item is present, rather the amount that they add up to indicates how full the canopy is. For example, the *Ficus polita* in Table 15E.2 has no young leaves and all mature leaves; however, because only about 75% of the crown is covered in leaves, mature leaves receive a score of 3. Similarly, this tree has fruit, about half of which is ripe and half of which is unripe; however, only about half of the crown contains fruit so the numbers given are 1 for unripe fruit and 1 for ripe fruit, leading to a 2/4 for quantity when these are added together. Since this method takes into account the quantity of each plant part, this is the method that Julie Teichroeb's research group uses at her field site in Uganda. Admittedly, both methods can be seen as subjective; therefore, the key is consistency in the observations, and among observers.

## Choosing a Phenological Sample

Phenological studies are normally conducted either along a set of transect lines or through an established study plot of several hundred square meters. Using a transect line, selecting all trees over 4 meters in height and within 5 meters on each side of the line may work to produce an adequate sampling. Chapman et al.

**Table 15E.1  Example of phenology scores for three trees where the scale for each plant part present must add to 4 (100%).**

| Tree | Mature Leaves | Young Leaves/Buds | Unripe Fruit | Ripe Fruit | Unripe Seed Pods | Ripe Seed Pods | Flower Buds | Flowers |
|---|---|---|---|---|---|---|---|---|
| *Ficus polita* 1 | 4 | 0 | 2 | 2 | | | | |
| *Albizia zygia* 4 | 3 | 1 | | | 1 | 3 | 0 | 0 |
| *Teclea noblis* 2 | 2 | 2 | 0 | 0 | | | 2 | 2 |

**Table 15E.2  Example of phenology scores for three trees with a measure of the quantity on the canopy incorporated.**

| Tree | Mature Leaf | Young Leaf/Bud | Total Leaves | Unripe Fruit | Ripe Fruit | Total Fruit | Unripe Seed Pod | Ripe Seed Pod | Total Seeds | Flower Bud | Flower | Total Flowers |
|---|---|---|---|---|---|---|---|---|---|---|---|---|
| *Ficus polita* 1 | 3 | 0 | 3 | 1 | 1 | 2 | | | | | | |
| *Albizia zygia* 4 | 2 | 1 | 3 | | | | 1 | 2 | 3 | 0 | 0 | 0 |
| *Teclea noblis* 2 | 2 | 2 | 4 | 0 | 0 | 0 | | | | 1 | 1 | 2 |

(1994) used such a technique in the Kibale Forest, Uganda, randomly selecting 200 meter long segments of the trail for regular phenological recording. However, forests can be patchy in their microhabitats, and different communities of plants may be present within the home range of your study groups. The trees present on your transect segments using this technique may only be a small subset of the tree species that are available and used by your study animals.

An alternative method is to actively try to obtain a sample of each tree species on your phenology route but to do so in a random manner. For example, if trees are tagged, you can put their numbers on slips of paper, and pull out slips to decide which trees end up on your phenology route, until you collect a specified number for a sample of each species (e.g., 5 individuals of each tree species). While this method is ideal for ensuring that you are collecting data on all the species of interest, it may only be possible if a botanical survey of the area has already been conducted.

Once you have a sampling method selected, you can proceed with producing a list of trees for your phenology route. Before beginning phenological monitoring, each of the trees needs to be measured, and if you are using a census strip, the species will need to be identified. Tree identification should be done by a knowledgeable herbalist or researcher (more information on this is presented in exercise 18). Measurements of trees usually include DBH (Diameter at Breast Height), H (Height), and HFB (Height of First Branch). In some forests and for some species, it may be necessary to attempt to determine the diameter above the buttresses of trees. This can be difficult but is generally not insolvable. In some cases, a GPS waypoint may also be obtained for each phenological tree in the sampling trail. Once the preliminary survey data are established, the phenological data can be regularly collected during a transect walk.

Phenological transect walks are conducted at routine intervals, often once or twice per month. However, you can also time your phenology surveys to occur immediately before or immediately after a few days of observation on a study group. In this way, you will have an idea of the food that was available to them during that set of observations.

## Analysis

Analysis of phenological data can be done in a diachronic mode such that measures of time between first leaf, first flower, and first mature fruit for individual species can be determined. This is simple for deciduous trees that undergo some period of dormancy, but evergreen species may have to be evaluated with "leaf traps" under them, and counts or weights of leaf fall evaluated weekly. For evergreen species, the most obvious diachronic factor is the time between first flowers and first fruits. A diachronic approach will also yield annual cycle graphs that show the numbers of species in leaf flush, flower bud, mature fruit, and others (see de Lampe et al. 1992; Frankie et al. 1974). In a short field study, such a wealth of diachronic data cannot be obtained, but sufficient data may be available to present graphic results over a three- or four-week period. It is more likely that a synchronic study will be the norm, and cross-sectional data presentations of percentage of, or number of, individuals in each phenological stage would be expected.

For more complex analyses where several years' worth of phenological records are available, the production of Colwell's P, C, and M indices is generally possible (Colwell 1974; Stearns 1981). The mathematics of calculating these indices are not simple; graduate and professional researchers are referred to the original articles for an explanation of the procedures and attendant cautions.

## The Exercise

The purpose of this exercise is to develop an understanding of phenology and vegetational censusing under natural conditions and to develop a phenological record for a field school site or another appropriate area. Proceed as follows:

A. Determine whether the field site has established transect lines or if it will be necessary to lay out your own lines (flagging tape is probably the most appropriate material to use for marking transects).

B. Design the transect layout and verify that it is feasible (i.e., it must not run over a cliff, through a lake, or over other impassible terrain!). The transect length can be variable, but it should be long enough to have a good probability of sampling most of the variant communities in the area, usually the rule is "the longer the better."

C. With the aid of a knowledgeable botanical assistant, each of the sample trees should be numbered, identified, and recorded in the site logbook. This information may already be available for the study area.

D. Walk the transect and collect data as detailed in the exercise discussion, and as required by your instructor. The instructor may set either a normal botanical phenology survey or a more intensive version. It is usually desirable to walk the transect several times during a preset period (e.g., a field school course of several weeks) to allow for some phenological progression to occur.

E. Inspect the data and calculate the numbers of species and individual trees in each state of the phenological cycle. If repeated surveys are done, can aspects of the cycles for different species be demonstrated?

F. Produce a final report for the exercise taking care to complete the analyses specified by the instructor.

# Example Phenology Sampling Worksheet

Observer: _____ Date: _____

Site: _____

Leaf Codes: D (dormant), Sh (shoots), Fl (flush of young leaves), Ml (mature leaf), Ol (old leaf)

Fruit/Flower Codes: DR (dormant reproductive), Fb (flower buds), Fl (flowers), If (immature fruit), Mf (mature fruit)

| Tree | Location | Leaf Status | Fruit Status | Notes |
|------|----------|-------------|--------------|-------|
|      |          |             |              |       |
|      |          |             |              |       |
|      |          |             |              |       |
|      |          |             |              |       |
|      |          |             |              |       |
|      |          |             |              |       |
|      |          |             |              |       |
|      |          |             |              |       |
|      |          |             |              |       |
|      |          |             |              |       |
|      |          |             |              |       |
|      |          |             |              |       |
|      |          |             |              |       |
|      |          |             |              |       |
|      |          |             |              |       |
|      |          |             |              |       |
|      |          |             |              |       |
|      |          |             |              |       |
|      |          |             |              |       |
|      |          |             |              |       |
|      |          |             |              |       |
|      |          |             |              |       |
|      |          |             |              |       |
|      |          |             |              |       |
|      |          |             |              |       |
|      |          |             |              |       |
|      |          |             |              |       |
|      |          |             |              |       |
|      |          |             |              |       |
|      |          |             |              |       |
|      |          |             |              |       |
|      |          |             |              |       |

# Example Advanced Phenology Worksheet

Observer: _____ Date: _____

Site: _____

See the following page for leaf and reproductive codes.

| Tree | Location | Leaf Quadrant Code | Fruit Quadrant Code | Fruit Quadrant Counts | Notes |
|------|----------|--------------------|---------------------|-----------------------|-------|
|  |  |  |  |  |  |
|  |  |  |  |  |  |
|  |  |  |  |  |  |
|  |  |  |  |  |  |
|  |  |  |  |  |  |
|  |  |  |  |  |  |
|  |  |  |  |  |  |
|  |  |  |  |  |  |
|  |  |  |  |  |  |
|  |  |  |  |  |  |
|  |  |  |  |  |  |
|  |  |  |  |  |  |
|  |  |  |  |  |  |
|  |  |  |  |  |  |
|  |  |  |  |  |  |
|  |  |  |  |  |  |
|  |  |  |  |  |  |
|  |  |  |  |  |  |
|  |  |  |  |  |  |
|  |  |  |  |  |  |
|  |  |  |  |  |  |
|  |  |  |  |  |  |
|  |  |  |  |  |  |
|  |  |  |  |  |  |
|  |  |  |  |  |  |
|  |  |  |  |  |  |
|  |  |  |  |  |  |
|  |  |  |  |  |  |
|  |  |  |  |  |  |
|  |  |  |  |  |  |
|  |  |  |  |  |  |

# Code Sheet for Fine-Grained Phenology

## Leaf

| | |
|---|---|
| L0 | dormant |
| L1 | initial bud |
| L2 | developing bud |
| L3 | mature bud |
| L4 | initial leaf |
| L5 | new leaf |
| L6 | juvenile leaf |
| L7 | full new leaf |
| L8 | mature leaf |
| L9 | old leaf |
| L10 | degenerate leaf |
| L11 | discarded leaf |

## Reproductives

| | |
|---|---|
| R0 | dormant |
| R1 | initial bud |
| R2 | developing bud |
| R3 | mature bud |
| R4 | initial flower |
| R5 | juvenile flower |
| R6 | mature flower |
| R7 | open flower |
| R8 | pollinated flower |
| R9 | petals discarded |
| R10 | small immature fruit (seed set) |
| R11 | larger juvenile fruit |
| R12 | full-sized immature fruit |
| R13 | staged ripening of fruit—1, 2, 3, 4 |
| R14 | fully ripe fruit |
| R15 | degenerate fruit |
| R16 | discarded fruit |

# EXERCISE 16

# A Home Range Survey
## What Is the Group's Home Range?
## A Comparison of Methods

Determination of the area that a primate individual or group ranges over is a basic data collection exercise that can become extremely complex in the analysis. To begin with, there are three related terms commonly employed in primatological studies: *home range; territory;* and *core area*. It is worth emphasizing that two of these are observational artifacts, and only one of them is present in the mind of the primate involved. This latter feature is "territory," most commonly defined as an area reserved for the exclusive use of an individual or group and defended against conspecifics. The territory may be perceived by the primate or primates as a "possession" to be defended. The terms territoriality or territorial behavior refer to the actions that animals take to defend their territory from conspecifics. It should be noted that most primate species are not strictly territorial and most show overlap in their area of use (i.e., home range) with conspecific groups. The other two concepts important in understanding ranging behavior, home range and core area, are arbitrary constructions of the observer. The "home range" is defined as the total area used by an individual or group and is usually determined by at least one year of following the study subjects, so all seasonal shifts are covered; however, longer periods of observation are always better. The "core area" is arbitrary to a degree and is generally defined as the area within the home range where the majority (or largest percentage) of time is spent. These are human creations and might not be recognized by the primates themselves. It is also worth noting that home ranges are almost always larger than territories, when they exist, which in turn, are larger than core areas. Many primates that are not territorial and show home range overlap with conspecifics may still aggressively defend the core area of their range, which is often the area with the best food resources.

Because most primates live in what we perceive as a home range, this exercise centers around the techniques used to determine a home range for a subject species, though if students are completing this exercise in the context of a field school, it will not be an annual range. It is acknowledged that more observation is better in determining the true home range of an animal group, but there is a point where more observation will only lead to small increases in the known home range. A relevant technique developed by Odum and Kuenzler (1955) for ornithology is based on this principle of diminishing returns. They assume that as the number of observations increases, the rate of increase in the home range area will decrease with each increment. This means that the home range area reaches toward an asymptotic approach to the "real" home range area, and they consequently and arbitrarily applied a "1% rule." This is the point on the curve where each added observation produces an increment of less than one percent of the area calculated as the final size. The purpose of this technique was not to estimate range size but to estimate the number of observations necessary to validly calculate the range area.

Lehner (1996) points out that ranges can be obtained through two methods: (1) direct observation, and (2) indirect methods, which include: tracks, capture-recapture, GPS collars, radio telemetry, camera traps, baits with ingestion dyes to color urine or feces, among other methods. We will only deal with the direct observation process in this exercise as the indirect methods are not often used by primatologists and frequently require capture. Application of the Odum and Kuenzler technique is much easier to apply to birds than mammals, where it has been estimated that radio telemetry would be the appropriate observational method. A discussion of the technique as well as the indirect methods of determining ranges can be found in Lehner (1996:510–521).

Home ranges can be calculated for lesser periods, as will be done in this exercise. "Ten-day ranges" were frequently used in early studies, as have been "monthly," "quarterly," and "seasonal" range collections. The simplest methodology involves recording the locations of subjects on a map plot of the study locality. This is easiest in an area that has been gridded with transect trails. Often these lines will be placed at 50 or 100 m intervals, providing a set of one hectare-sized blocks and making the calculation of the range straightforward. Individual or group location can also be recorded at set time intervals using a handheld GPS device. The points that are obtained can later be downloaded into a GIS program (e.g., ArcGIS by Esri, Inc.) and a grid can be placed over the top of the points. If continuous observations are taken, and complete day ranges obtained, a simple process of plotting the set of day ranges on the map grid will enable the researcher to draw a line around the area delineating the "home" range. This can be done in two ways:

1. through counting the number of hectare blocks in which the subjects are seen, or
2. by drawing a "least polygon" around the areas used, and counting quarter or half hectare units where the polygon line crosses a block.

Figure 16E.1 shows the difference between these two processes for a small grid.

A: Block Count                    B: Least Polygon

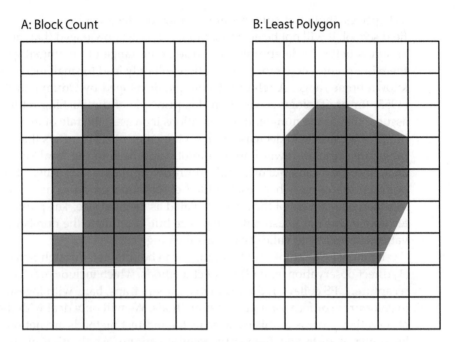

**Figure 16E.1** Two methods of delineating home range. "A" presents a block count of 14 hectares, while "B" with the least polygon encloses a larger area of 17.5 hectares.

Alternatively, if GPS units and GIS programs are going to be used, quadrats may not need to be utilized at all. The ranging points obtained from your study animals can be plotted and a "minimum convex polygon" method (MCP) can be employed (Hayne 1949). With this technique, the outer locations provided by the scattering of GPS points are connected to form a convex polygon. The area of the enclosed shape can then be calculated in the GIS program.

In Figure 16E.1, the block count method (also known as the "grid cell method") provides a more conservative estimate of home range size than the least polygon method, which may be more accurate. The degree of accuracy provided by these methods, however, is greatly affected by the size of the quadrats, in that a grid with smaller quadrats will be more accurate. The MCP is a common method of home range calculation in primatology; however, it is sensitive to the presence of outliers and can overestimate home range to a large extent, especially if the animals make long forays to infrequently visited areas (Grueter et al. 2009).

Primatologists also regularly apply kernel estimator techniques to calculate ranging areas for their study subjects. The benefit of these is that they use nonparametric statistics to determine the probability of finding the study group/individual in a particular location (Worton 1989). Though these types of methods are often considered the most accurate, this is not always the case since they can be affected by small sample size. Also, fragmented forest areas may be misrepresented by these techniques (Boyle et al. 2009). Most authors recommend using more than one method for calculating the home range of your study subjects due to the benefits and drawbacks of each. Note that as technology and the use of GIS expand, new methods for calculating home ranges are being published that can provide more fine-grained analysis than some of the traditional methods described here. Your choice of method should be dependent on your study questions and other variables.

## The Exercise

The purpose of this exercise is to calculate "short-duration" home range areas and compare methods during a field practical study. The main operative assumption is that the exercise would not be conducted as a single project, but would be coincident with other projects.

If observations are to be done by hand in the field:

A. Use a topographical map or a satellite image of the study area. On a clear plastic transparency sheet, draw out the transect lines and create a grid overlay (50 m × 50 m, 100 m × 100 m, or other). Size can be adjusted as necessary for that particular field site to complete the exercise.

B. During observational data collection (or even after observations are completed from your fieldnotes), mark the locations where the study subjects have been observed on the grid. It may be appropriate to distinguish between levels of use for each hectare by placing a count of encounters, or of hours observed, in the block.

C. Employing the two techniques illustrated in Figure 16E.1, calculate a simple count of hectares, and a least polygon, estimate the home range area as you have observed it. An important query may be answered from your data: Will an increase in the number of points used in each method improve the estimate of range size? Perhaps you should calculate the area with 10, 20, and 30 location points.

D. Prepare a report in the proper format, and with any further analyses, as specified by the instructor.

If a handheld GPS unit is used to collect data points:

A. Ensure that you are familiar with the functions and use of your GPS unit. It is also important to consider signal reception and the accuracy of the waypoints you are recording. Be sure to read the manual thoroughly and consult publications such as Hughes (2003) for more information on using these systems.

B. Choose the method that will be used to collect GPS waypoints of group location. The timing of these points, where they will be taken within the group, and how they will be labeled all need to be considered. It is common for primatologists to record a GPS point at 15-minute intervals during follows and to take them in the approximate center of the study group, but some other considerations may be appropriate to your study. In terms of labeling your points, a good system is to include some denotation of the study group and perhaps a reference to date and time.

C. After data collection, download your waypoints in a GIS program. Often a program to plot waypoints will come with your GPS unit; however, programs like ArcView (an open-source program such as QGIS is also popular) provide many more features and options for dealing with your data. Using the GIS program, superimpose a grid onto the scatter of GPS points you collected (e.g., 50 m × 50 m, 100 m × 100 m, or other). The locations of repeated waypoints show heavy use of particular areas.

D. Calculate home range size using the three techniques discussed above to compare their output. For the block count, the number of grid cells with at least one waypoint can be counted and the area in hectares calculated. The least polygon method can also be assessed by using the grid cells and determining the number of hectares covered. Only the scatter of waypoints is needed to assess MCP using the outermost points, and the area within the polygon can be calculated by your GIS program. Again, an important query may be answered from your data: Will an increase in the number of points used for each method improve the estimate of range size? Perhaps you should calculate the area with 10, 20, and 30 location points.

E. Prepare a report in the proper format, and with any further analyses, as specified by the instructor.

# EXERCISE 17

# Ecological Sample Plots and Indices

Any study of ecological relationships in primatology will eventually require the development of a vegetation plot or a comparative set of plots to quantify resources available to primates. Ecological measurements can help to address larger questions about how primate populations are limited by the availability of food resources. Two major factors influencing primate behavioral ecology are variations in resource abundance and resource diversity. Because most primates rely heavily on plants as major components of their diet, both measurements provide important predictors of primate biodiversity that are critical not only to our understanding of behavior but also to inform conservation management decisions.

Not surprisingly, there are many different methods used to sample plants and even variations in the methods used for different communities of plants. Given the methodological and contextual variation, it is important to keep in mind that you must choose the best sampling technique for a given ecological system, and that not every method will work in every situation. It is important to ensure that the methods used to quantify primate habitats are appropriate for the question(s) being addressed, the scale of the study, the behavioral ecology of the species or population (e.g., small quadrats of $10 \times 10$ m may not effectively measure the habitat of a large chimpanzee community that ranges over several km$^2$), and the habitat type and associated logistics (e.g., mountainous, flat, impenetrable forest). For this exercise, we review two of the most common types of plot sampling methods: line transect and quadrat sampling.

Samples are usually taken with a standard sampling unit of some kind and are distributed using either random or stratified sampling. This ensures that all the samples represent the same area of the habitat each time. We refer the reader to Ganzhorn et al. (2011) and Southwood and Henderson (2000) for further information on methods to implement multiple plot samples.

# Line Transect Sampling

Transect sampling is one of the most widespread ecological techniques for sampling both plants and animals. To implement this technique, the investigator establishes a line (i.e., the transect line) between two points (Figure 17E.1). There are several ways to conduct a transect sample. All individual plants on the transect line may be counted and their position along the transect recorded, or all individuals may be counted within a given distance (e.g., 5 m on each side) of the transect line and their distances along and to the side of the line recorded. It is also common to place quadrats (see below) at specific distances along the transect and collect data within each quadrat. The length of the transect line and the distance to each side can vary according to habitat type, tree density, and landscape logistics, but Ganzhorn et al. (2011) recommend a transect line of 100 m with 5 m on each side, for a total sampling area of 0.1 hectares (abbreviated as ha).

For most primate habitats, a "plant" is usually equal to a tree, measured using the standard diameter at breast height (DBH) of about 1.3 m from the ground. Some tree trunks flare outwards at their base, and most flaring occurs below breast height (at least in temperate zones). Trees could have similar biomass but have different diameters at their bases; therefore, the diameter above the base provides a more reliable measure of tree abundance when sampling different kinds of trees. Rather than measuring all trees within a given area, most studies only measure trees >10–30 cm DBH to provide a good representation of habitat ecology, though minimum DBH can vary depending on the habitat type, size, and density of trees. Unless you have special forestry measurement tools, you usually first measure the CBH (the circumference at breast height) and then convert it to DBH (D = circumference/$\pi$); therefore, you would convert your minimum DBH to a minimum CBH.

It is important to have replicate transects within the same area (in the same direction, if possible), placed either using random or stratified sampling methods to provide sufficient data to evaluate the habitat. Abundance measures are calculated based on the CBH of all trees within the sampling area with a predetermined minimum CBH (e.g., 5 cm, 10 cm, 20 cm, or other). Transect sampling is appropriate for thick tropical forests where logistics make quadrats more difficult to set due to restricted accessibility, allowing for a more representative sample; however, choice of starting point is not usually random but opportunistic (Ganzhorn et al. 2011).

# Quadrat Sampling

Quadrat sampling is a method used to intensively sample a subset of a system to obtain a representative sample. The technique involves selecting square (or sometimes rectangular) areas (quadrats) of a specific size within a study area

(Figure 17E.1) and implementing multiple quadrats of uniform size in a random or stratified way across the area to ensure that the data represent an unbiased picture of the larger habitat. Quadrat size can vary dramatically, anywhere from 1 to 100 m$^2$ or more. The choice of size depends on the vegetation type (smaller sizes for more herbaceous vegetation, and larger for taller trees) and your research questions (e.g., smaller sizes for measuring seedling recruitment). Once established, all individual plants above a predetermined size are counted and measured within each quadrat.

Quadrats are useful in many habitats so long as all four corner points and everything in between are accessible, and they offer the flexibility of allowing for adjustment in plot size according to relevant microhabitats if required. However, quadrats of different shapes can produce different density estimates (Ganzhorn et al. 2011), so it is important for them to remain consistent in size and shape as much as possible.

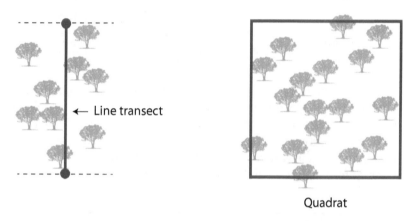

← Line transect

Quadrat

**Figure 17E.1** A diagrammatic representation of line transect sampling and quadrat sampling.

## Common Vegetative Measures

There are several standard and straightforward vegetative calculations that will provide information on density and abundance based on the data collected from line transect or quadrat samples:

| | |
|---|---|
| **Species richness:** | total number of different plant/tree species within a range or area sampled |
| **Species abundance:** | the number of individuals of species A |

**Area of an individual tree**: diameter = circumference$/\pi$
radius (r) = diameter$/2$
area = $\pi r^2$

**Relative abundance**:

$$\frac{\text{\# of individuals of species A}}{\text{\# of individuals of all species counted}}$$

e.g., $\dfrac{\text{\# figs}}{\text{\# all trees}}$

**Density**:

$$\frac{\text{\# of individuals counted}}{\text{area sampled (m}^2)}$$

**Basal area**: total area of species A (the sum of the area of each individual tree of species A)

**Relative Basal Area**:

$$\frac{\text{total basal area species A}}{\text{total basal area of all trees in the sampled area}}$$

**Dominance**:

$$\frac{\text{total basal area species A}}{\text{total area sampled}}$$

Each measure will provide different information about the habitat sampled. When analyzing these data based on several plot samples, the investigator can determine the broader abundance and density of the primate food supply in a given habitat.

We refer the reader to Henderson (2003) and Ganzhorn et al. (2011) for further information on habitat sampling methods.

# Analysis Using Dispersion and Diversity Indices

There are several indices of ecological complexity, usually in the form of an index or coefficient of dispersion, which can be applied to vegetation plots that yield useful information applicable to problems in primate behavior and socioecology. These "indices of dispersion" can also be used to measure the spread of animals throughout the environment, and at a fine-grained analysis, they can assist in studies of the temporal patterns of habitat usage. "Indices of diversity" can determine the effective number of types (usually of a species) within a community while accounting for the distribution of individuals.

The most basic and useful calculations for the distribution of animal and plant species within the community are Morisita's Index of Dispersion and the Standardized Morisita Index. For comparing the species composition of sample plots, two calculations provide measures of similarity: Morisita's Index of Similarity and Morisita's Simplified Index of Similarity. To determine species diversity, the Shannon-Wiener Diversity Index (also referred to as the "Shannon Index" or the "Shannon-Weaver Index") is commonly used.

All of these indices presume the existence of a set of sample plots for which there are some form of frequency data. The most common type of data is a count of the number of individuals of a group (for an estimate of group dispersion) or of species present (for estimates of the dispersion pattern or vegetation diversity). The data required for the indices described here are only counts of identified species.

## Morisita's Index of Dispersion

Morisita's Index of Dispersion (Morisita 1962, represented by $I_d$) can be applied to individual species (both plant and animal), and provides an "index" that is independent of population density, though it is affected by sample size. It does have a known sampling distribution, and hence, a version of the chi-square test can be employed to validate the results (see Krebs 1999). The formula for $I_d$ is:

$$I_d = n\left(\frac{\sum x^2 - \sum x}{(\sum x)^2 - \sum x}\right)$$

Where: $n$ = sample size, the number of quadrats measured
$\sum x$ = the sum of the counts in each quadrat
$\sum x^2$ = is the sum of quadrat counts squared

These values can be most easily calculated and organized in the same fashion as for a standard deviation (see chapter 6).

## Morisita's Index of Similarity

Morisita's Index of Similarity (Morisita 1959) measures the similarity between two communities or sample sets. Students are advised not to confuse this with his Index of Dispersion. They are distinct calculations and evaluate different data. The index is traditionally represented as $C_\lambda$ but has occasionally appeared in the literature as $I_s$. In either case, it can be interpreted as a probability statement. The index measures the probability that an individual organism drawn from one sample, and one drawn from a second sample will be of the same species, divided by the probability that two individuals drawn from either sample one or two will be of the same species. The formula is moderately complicated as follows:

$$C_\lambda = \frac{2 \sum X_{i_1} X_{i_2}}{(\lambda_1 + \lambda_2) N_1 N_2}$$

231

Where: $X_{i_1}$ = Number of individuals of species $i$ in sample one

$X_{i_2}$ = Number of individuals of species $i$ in sample two

$N_1$ = Total number of individuals (all species) in sample one

$N_2$ = Total number of individuals (all species) in sample two

$$\lambda_1 = \frac{\Sigma\left[X_{i_1}\left(X_{i_1}-1\right)\right]}{N_1\left(N_1-1\right)}$$

and

$$\lambda_2 = \frac{\Sigma\left[X_{i_2}\left(X_{i_2}-1\right)\right]}{N_2\left(N_2-1\right)}$$

Note that this is a calculation for only one species and would be repeated for each additional species. Morisita's Index of Similarity is nearly independent of sample size, is exceedingly robust, and is largely considered to be the best overall measure of similarity for ecological use.

---

## Shannon-Wiener Diversity Index

The Shannon-Wiener Diversity Index (H) measures the relationship between the number of species ("species richness") and the relative frequency of these species (the "equitability") within a habitat (Spellerberg 1991). The formula is as follows:

$$H = \Sigma\left[(p_i) \times \ln(p_i)\right]$$

Where: $p_i$ = proportion of the total sample represented by species i (divide # of individuals of species i by the total # of samples)

$\ln$ = natural logarithm

$S$ = species richness (see below)

The maximum diversity value that H can reach is expressed as $H_{max}$ in the following equation:

$$H_{max} = \ln(S)$$

The $H_{max}$ will only be reached if all species are equally represented in the community, expressed as E, representing evenness or equitability:

$$E = H/H_{max}$$

# The Exercises

These exercises are to provide practice in (a) ecological calculations, and (b) the use of indices of similarity to evaluate the dispersion of a species.

## Ecological Calculations

To practice ecological calculations, you will employ the transect sampling method. First, find a wooded area nearby where you can conduct some measurements safely; ask permission if needed. You will plot a line transect sampling plotline of 50 m, with a sampling area of 5 m on each side, for a total sampling area of 50 m × 10 m, or 500 m². If this plot size is not feasible, the instructor will provide alternate measurements. After marking and roping off your transect, you will measure all trees within your sampling area that are >20 cm CBH (or as determined by the instructor). To determine diversity, you would normally want to be able to identify the different tree species within your area of interest. You can look closely at features such as leaves (color, shape, texture) and bark (color, texture) to identify different species within your sampling area. You can consult online resources or regional tree identification guides to help you identify particular species, but if you cannot identify a species after consulting appropriate resources, you can call them species A, B, C, or other. Remember to remove all flags and string from your sampling area when complete.

Use the vegetation measurement and calculation sheet at the end of the exercise to help you collect the data and complete your calculations. Then write a brief report describing what each calculation can tell us about the (hypothetical) primate food supply.

## Index of Similarity

To practice using indices of similarity, proceed as follows:

A. Determine whether the field site has established sample plots, or if it will necessitate laying out your own.

B. Design the sample plot layout and verify that it can be examined in the time available. A suggested plot size and a minimum DBH may be imposed by the instructor.

C. With the aid of a knowledgeable botanical assistant, each of the sample trees should be numbered, identified, and recorded in the site logbook. This may already be available for the sample plot.

D. Inspect the data and calculate the index of dispersion for the most common species, and for the least common. Calculate the index of similarity and the percentage similarity for the sample plots.

E. Produce a final report for the exercise taking care to complete the analyses specified by the instructor.

# Example Line Transect Data Collection Sheet

Date _____ Area _____ GPS location _____

| Species | CBH (cm) | DBH (cm) | DBH (m) | Area |
|---------|----------|----------|---------|------|
|  |  |  |  |  |
|  |  |  |  |  |
|  |  |  |  |  |
|  |  |  |  |  |
|  |  |  |  |  |
|  |  |  |  |  |
|  |  |  |  |  |
|  |  |  |  |  |

# Example Vegetation Calculations

Total Number of Trees _____ Species Richness _____

Total Area Sampled ($m^2$) _____

Total Tree Density ($m^2$) _____

Total Tree Basal Area ($m^2$) _____

| Species | Abundance | Density | Relative Abundance | Basal Area | Relative Basal Area | Dominance |
|---------|-----------|---------|--------------------|------------|---------------------|-----------|
|  |  |  |  |  |  |  |
|  |  |  |  |  |  |  |
|  |  |  |  |  |  |  |
|  |  |  |  |  |  |  |
|  |  |  |  |  |  |  |
|  |  |  |  |  |  |  |
|  |  |  |  |  |  |  |
|  |  |  |  |  |  |  |

# EXERCISE 18

# Vegetative Sampling and Voucher Specimens

One of the normative activities for any field study is, or at least should be, the collection of plant samples for identification, and, secondarily, for the maintenance of a herbarium collection. This exercise is not intended to fulfill all of these objectives, but merely to provide experiential learning in the processes and practices of collecting adequate samples. By an "adequate" sample, it is implied that the amount of material and the extent of the structures sampled are sufficient to enable a herbarium technician to identify it to the species level. Secondly, should a researcher collect a plant new to science, sufficient material is needed to provide the requisite "voucher specimens" that will serve as the future "type" specimens. These two steps are normally sequential, with the second triggered by a response of an "unidentified/new plant" from the herbarium. Lest you think this unlikely, in 1996 the Budongo Forest Project forwarded two new species to the botanical literature from a thoroughly explored forest that has been intensively studied, and has been under a managed logging regime since the 1920s (V. Reynolds, personal communication).

## Plant Specimen Sampling

You have just seen a primate consume the leaves of a plant, and your research assistant cannot identify the species—what do you do now? You want to collect a specimen from the plant and have it identified at a herbarium. How much material do you need to collect? One botanist of Jim Paterson's acquaintance, perhaps facetiously, said "The whole thing!" And to an extent, that injunction is an indicator that the person conducting the identification would like to have too much rather than too little material. For instance, it is generally appropriate to attempt to collect not a single leaf but a whole leaf cluster, not a single flower but a whole flowering mass. An excellent sample would include—for small plants, the leaves, flowers, fruit (in season); and for some varieties, the root, rhizome, or tuber. At minimum, a leaf cluster may be the smallest acceptable sample. Once the sample is collected, it is likely that it cannot be immediately presented to the botanical technician, but must be preserved in a manner that retains as much information as possible. The normal process utilized is drying in a plant press.

A plant press consists of four components: two outside plates, ventilators, dryers (blotting paper or felt), and a mechanism to apply pressure to the stack. Commercially manufactured presses are available at modest cost, but a perfectly adequate one can be constructed of two pieces of plywood (roughly 30 × 45 cm or 12 × 18 inches), two webbing straps (with buckles), and a pile of corrugated cardboard in the same size as the outer boards, blotters, and newspaper. The standard pressing process involves the placement of the sample between sheets of newspaper, a blotter and cardboard on each side of the specimen, and stacking specimen sets between the pressboards. The web straps are then used to apply a strong compression to the stack. The loaded press is then placed on edge, with the cardboard corrugations aligned vertically, in a location that provides a flow of warm dry air. In the field, this may be in the rafters of the field hut, on a rack beside the cooking fire, or suspended at a safe distance above a gas lamp. It is advisable to replace the dryers and ventilators at least once per day to avoid the development of mold on the specimens, as well as to speed up the process. Some plant materials will adhere strongly to paper, and others, particularly large succulent or fleshy plant materials, cannot be dried satisfactorily without cutting the specimen into appropriate forms. In the former case, directly drying the specimen on a mounting sheet with a layer of wax paper may suffice; in the latter, cutting the specimen so as to create an outside layer that can be spread out flat is the common procedure. Alternatively, succulents and fleshy plant materials can be submerged in sample bottles under FAA (formal-acetic-alcohol, see recipe below), which will also preserve the original colors of the specimen.

If the materials for building your own plant press are not available, it is possible to preserve samples by other means. In Ghana, Julie Teichroeb and Tania Saj managed to preserve samples in a creative way: pressed in newspaper, with an upside-down table on top, weighed down with rocks. These specimens were not mountable afterward but could be identified by the local herbarium.

---

### FAA (formal-acetic-alcohol)

- equal parts of water and 95% ethanol (may or may not be denatured)
- add formaldehyde (40%) and acetic acid (glacial 35%) each in the amount of 2% of the volume of water and alcohol mixture; preferably store in dark bottles

---

# Fieldnotes

Whenever specimens are collected, accurate information as to the locale, longitude and latitude, and the surroundings of the specimen—in particular, the plant community type, associated plants, altitude, slope of the ground, nature of the soil, its moisture content and other pertinent information—should be recorded.

For the specimen itself, the observer should record the: (1) average size of specimens, (2) color and pattern of the flower, (3) nature of the bark (for trees)—pattern, external color, color when slashed—and information on the sap—smell, color, texture (i.e., latex-like), and (4) color information on the leaves in case the specimen fades during drying. Photographs of the plant *in situ*, as well as focused shots of each of the plant parts, can be extremely useful to botanists as well since the drying process can alter colors and change the shape and size of the fruit (a standard color card or a photograph with such a card next to the specimen is often useful and appropriate).

## Mounting Voucher Specimens

Standard mounting paper for herbarium use is a sulfur-free heavy paper of 30 cm × 40 cm (11.5 in × 16.5 in) in size. The specimen may be folded to fit onto the sheet and can be attached with special "herbarium tape," a diluted white glue mixture, or one of the newer herbarium fixative sprays. In any case, the dried plant is affixed to the paper, the field note data are transferred directly to the sheet, and, if necessary, an envelope for loose components is attached. This entire sheet constitutes the voucher specimen for the plant.

## The Exercise

The purpose of this exercise is to provide practice in the collection, preparation, and mounting of plant specimens relevant to a behavioral ecology study of a primate species.

   A. Prepare a listing of specimens to collect; it might be most appropriate to sample the species that are fed on by the local primates.

   B. Proceed to collect samples of the species on your list; make certain the sample is large enough to provide a complete leaf cluster, add fruit and/or flowers if available, and prepare fieldnotes.

   C. With the aid of a knowledgeable botanical assistant each of the samples should be numbered, identified, and recorded in fieldnotes and logbooks.

   D. Place specimens into the plant press and dry them for several days. Using appropriate mounting media, affix the specimens to herbarium pages and transfer the field note data.

   E. Produce a final report for the exercise as specified by the instructor, and submit it with the herbarium samples.

# Applied Study Projects
## Branching out into Research Design

The following three exercises are intended as projects for the development of research designs and/or as small research projects in themselves. Each presents a research problem and makes some suggestions as to how it may be organized, but the development of an acceptable design and protocol is the exercise.

### EXERCISE 19
A Spatial Locational Study

### EXERCISE 20
Exploring Postural Congruence

### EXERCISE 21
A Handedness Study

# EXERCISE 19

# A Spatial Locational Study

One relevant question for any primate study is: "Do the individual animals move evenly through their environments, or do they have areas and pathways of preferred usage?" Intuitively, since we recognize such patterns in our lifestyles, we would posit that they do show preferential space use. However, as scientists we would like to be able to show support for this conclusion, as well as investigate the patterns that may be employed by individuals, by different sex and age groups, and so on. For example, there may be a prime location in an enclosure that all animals would like to occupy but because the dominant individuals can displace others, they get the first choice and spend their resting time in this favored spot. A large number of possibilities are open to development once the basic concept of locational studies has been selected.

This exercise is straightforward and can be carried out with primate populations in zoological enclosures. The first operation after the selection of the study group is to "map" the enclosure areas. The map may be simple gridding of the enclosure floor into quadrants (just the four quarters) or 6, 8, 9, 12, 16, or more quadrats (smaller squares). In more complex enclosures, particularly those that offer substantial use of the third dimension, a set of cubic measures would be more appropriate. It is unlikely that the facility will be amenable to physically marking these divisions on the enclosure so the most appropriate technique is to create a map that uses clearly observable features to establish boundaries between quadrants/quadrats. Observational techniques such as focal animal sampling could be used, but the interval process of a group-oriented scan sampling can be used to collect large amounts of data on all individuals in a relatively short period.

Once the protocol is established, the mapping is done, and the data-recording technique is selected, some consideration of the analytical issues should be included, before the start of the collecting phase. The data collected from this study, at least in the design pattern suggested here, is not amenable to simple statistical testing.

The content of this exercise was contributed by Dr. Sue Taylor Parker, Anthropology, Sonoma State University, as a component in a larger full-term observational project. It has been modified from the original form.

The most appropriate analysis where there are data represented as frequency counts in a large number of cells, whether it is arranged linearly or as a row and column table, is the G-test of goodness-of-fit. The *G-test* or *G-statistic* is perhaps more typically found in social science statistics texts as the $\chi^2$ (chi-square) table test. An important consideration for the employment of this statistic is the interpretation of the probability value derived. If the value of "G" reaches the critical level (usually the $\leq 0.05$ criterion) this signifies rejection of the null hypothesis, which is always that there *is no* effect (of location) in the data, or alternatively, that the frequency of observations in each quadrat is not significantly different. An appropriate interpretation then is that the alternative hypothesis (that there *is* an effect of location) may be accepted. This is one of the circumstances where the test process is interpreted in a different fashion to the common chi-square test. It is possible to test individual cells against each other using the regular chi-square but with a large number of cells the number of tests to be run increases rapidly. An excellent explanation of the G-test along with an online tool for calculating it is provided in McDonald (2014) at http://www.biostathandbook.com/gtestgof.html.

With these cautions in mind, the student is invited to construct a research design for a spatial locational study. The three critical components are:

1. Construction of an appropriate cellular division of the study environment

2. Selection of an appropriate observational protocol

3. A statement of the analytical processes to be employed

Once the research proposal is approved by the instructor, the student might be directed to seek approval of the project from the appropriate Animal Care Committee and to carry out the study, producing a standard scientific report.

# EXERCISE 20

# Exploring Postural Congruence

Have you ever noticed individuals in reasonable proximity to or interacting with one another, employing the same postural positions? This phenomenon is commonly present in herds, flocks, and schools of animals, and is most often seen as a coordinated movement. It is, however, often ignored as a behavior pattern in more individualistic species such as primates. Sharing of postures is such a common human practice that 35 years ago Scheflen (1964, 1965, 1972) proposed that such interactions should be called "postural congruence" and be treated as a communicative adjunct to speech. Scheflen went on to suggest that the pattern of postural sequencing was linked to the particular language used by each individual. He was suggesting that the patterns were culturally conditioned. In the past, this study of nonverbal signaling was typically only employed in human psychiatry and psychology. However, studies by Boyd (1998) and by Jazrawi (2000) confirmed that postural congruence also functions as part of nonhuman primate communication. Recent work has shown that these imitative behaviors are likely important for socialization and learning in chimpanzees and may even be seen between species (Sauciuc et al. 2017; Persson et al. 2018).

Postural congruence, abbreviated to "PC" and not to be confused with the "post-conflict" discussed in exercise 11, has also been called "postural echo" (Beattie and Beattie 1981). PC can be grouped under the more general pattern of "model and mimic" in that one individual adopts a posture (becomes the model), and a second individual subsequently moves into the same posture (is the mimic). PC can be normal or parallel with both individuals orientated in the same direction, or in a mirror image form that most commonly occurs with the two subjects facing each other.

The psychiatry-psychology literature argues that the use of PC is related to either attempt at personal gain by an individual, or to signal agreement or solidarity between individuals. Thus, in nonhuman primates, PC might be used by members of a group to indicate unity in the face of challenges, or agreement with a movement decision, or by individual's intent on social manipulation to attempt to rise in rank, or as means of obtaining access to some resource controlled by another. Interpretation of the behavior is context-specific. Baboons and chimpanzees waiting to secure a morsel of meat from a prey carcass adopt the posture of the "possessor" of the carcass. Females wanting to touch or play with a newborn adopt the same posture as the mother to get closer. There are innumerable instances of recorded postural congruence, but it is rarely a subject of study in itself.

PC may be divided into "complete" or whole-body congruence and "partial" or half-body congruence where only the upper *or* lower body and limbs are in the same postures. Researchers can also record the identity of the "model" and the "mimic" in situations where the sequence of events is observed and analyze these patterns later. Perhaps high-ranking animals are more likely to be models, and lower-ranking animals seeking favor with dominants are more likely to mimic. PC may also occur in differing patterns associated with age and sex categories, or may differ depending on whether the animals have female bonded or nonfemale bonded social systems.

The exercise is to search the literature and construct a research design (i.e., a proposal) to study the role or effect of PC in a social group. The design requires:

1. Clear and careful definition of terms
2. Construction of a useful ethogram and a "posturogram"
3. Detailing of the variables to be recorded
4. How the analysis will be conducted

Care needs to be taken in setting the observational "boundary conditions," such as: What is the maximum distance where two individuals can be considered as still "interacting" and not just being in congruence by chance? What is the chance probability that two individuals are in postural congruence because they are performing the same behavior? These are just two of the possible confounding situations in this type of study.

The instructor may provide a more detailed set of requirements for the completion of the proposal document. Conduct of the study after approval by an Animal Care Committee may also be the major focus of a senior or graduate exercise.

# EXERCISE 21

# A Handedness Study

Humans demonstrate a strong population-level asymmetry in hand use, with over 90% of people showing right-handedness (Annett 1987). This is due to the lateralized functioning of our nervous system and left-hemisphere specialization in our brains (De Vleeschouwer et al. 1995). The questions of *when* and *why* this hemisphere specialization evolved in the human lineage are ongoing; however, many studies to date support that this trait is controlled by genetic and environmental factors. There are several hypotheses for what might have triggered such extreme lateralization in humans (reviewed in Prieur et al. 2019).

Research addressing handedness in the nonhuman primates has helped shed light on these questions (Prieur et al. 2019) and observation of hand use in different tasks is relatively simple using animals in various environments. Most species of nonhuman primates tested have shown individual-level biases in hand use (Poindexter et al. 2018) and population-level asymmetries are rare. For example, chimpanzees have been found to show population-level hand preferences but the hand that is favored differs for different tool-use tasks (Lonsdorf and Hopkins 2005). What is often lateralized at the population-level for nonhuman primates are eye preferences, which do indicate an asymmetry of processing in the brain (Rogers 2018).

The exercise here is to design a study that would measure hand use in a nonhuman primate population in the most valid way possible. Some things to be considered when designing a study on handedness are:

1. *The hypotheses for the evolution of handedness that are going to be tested.*

2. *The types of tasks that are going to be recorded.* An example of a type of task is bimanual actions. These tend to elicit more of a hand preference than unimanual actions. The definition of bimanual action would be one where both hands are being used in different roles . . . , such as an activity where one hand is holding an object and the other hand is manipulating it. It may be best to record all hand use, however, and sort the data later based on task type and how many hands were involved.

3. *How hand use will be recorded.* An example of a type of recording method that would be ideal to measure handedness is focal animal sampling. This is because many tasks that animals use their hands for take time. Thus, they have duration and scan sampling or a similar recording method may not capture them all. Complex bimanual tasks may be best recorded using video, however, so that each manipulation is captured.

4. *The best method of analysis.* Most studies use the Handedness Index (Hopkins 1999), which allows you to tally all hand use by an individual and produce a number where -1 would be a completely left-handed individual and +1 would be a completely right-handed individual.

The instructor may provide a more detailed set of requirements for the completion of the study design. This could lead to a proposal document but the conduct of the study after approval by an Animal Care Committee may also be the major focus of a senior or graduate exercise.

# Appendix

## Summary of Video Resources

Video files of primates are provided in the online supplementary materials for this book. See **waveland.com**. Several species were filmed with permission at the Toronto Zoo. These videos are useful for testing out the data collection techniques in the exercises. The table on the following page provides details on the species in each file, the duration of the film, the difficulty level of recording the behavior of individuals (based on their speed, sociality, or other variables), the type of data collection technique that the file would be best used for, and notes on what is contained in the film. Files of the same duration are presented together, in increasing levels of difficulty.

**Note:** Even though each video file is suggested as ideal for a certain data collection technique, these files can, and should, be used to practice multiple techniques.

**Table A.1   Information for video files.**

| File # | Duration (min.) | Difficulty Level | Species | Ideal For | Notes |
|---|---|---|---|---|---|
| 1 | 5:00 | Low | Ring-tailed lemur | Focal-animal sampling | Male in the center of the frame in view the whole time |
| 2 | | Medium | Baboons | Focal-animal sampling | Two individuals grooming |
| 3 | | Medium | Baboons | Scan sampling | Whole enclosure |
| 4 | | High | Golden-lion tamarins | Focal-animal sampling | Individual on right in view the whole time |
| 5 | | High | Golden-lion tamarins | Scan sampling | Whole enclosure |
| 6 | 6:50 | Low | White-handed gibbon | Focal-animal sampling | One male kept in view |
| 7 | 10:00 | Low | White-faced saki | Focal-animal sampling | One male kept in view, housed with a sloth |
| 8 | | Low | Gorilla | Focal-animal sampling | One male kept in view |
| 9 | | Medium | Orangutans | Scan sampling | Two males kept in view the whole time |
| 10 | | Medium | Baboon | Focal-animal sampling | One male kept in view |
| 11 | | Medium | Common marmoset | Focal-animal sampling | One individual kept in view |
| 12 | | High | Golden-lion tamarins | Focal-animal sampling | One individual kept in view |
| 13 | 15:00 | Low | Gorilla | Focal-animal sampling | One male kept in view |
| 14 | | High | Golden-lion tamarins | Scan sampling | Whole enclosure |
| 15 | 20:00 | Medium | Baboon | Focal-animal sampling | One female kept in view |
| 16 | 25:00 | Medium | Orangutan | Focal-animal sampling | One male kept in view |

# Bibliography

Aardal, E., and Holm, A. C. 1995. Cortisol in saliva-reference ranges and relation to cortisol in serum. *Clinical Chemistry and Laboratory Medicine, 33*(12), 927–932.

Alcock, J. 1989. *Animal behavior: An evolutionary approach* (4th ed.). Sinauer Associates.

Alexander, R. D. 1975. The search for a general theory of behavior. *Behavioral Science, 20*(2), 77–100.

Allan, A. T. L., Bailey, A. L., and Hill, R. A. 2020. Habituation is not neutral or equal: Individual differences in tolerance suggest an overlooked personality trait. *Science Advances, 6*(28), eaaz0870.

Altmann, J. 1974. Observational study of behavior: Sampling methods. *Behaviour, 49*(3/4), 227–267.

Altmann, J., and Alberts, S. 1987. Body mass and growth rates in a wild primate population. *Oecologia, 72*(1), 15–20.

Altmann, S. A. 1968. Sociobiology of rhesus monkeys III: The basic communication network. *Behaviour, 32*(1–3), 19–49.

Amsler, S. J., 2010. Energetic costs of territorial boundary patrols by wild chimpanzees. *American Journal of Primatology, 72*(2), 93–103.

Ancrenaz, M., Setchell, J. M., and Curtis, D. J. 2003. Handling, anaesthesia, health evaluation and biological sampling. In J. M. Setchell and D. J. Curtis (Eds.), *Field and laboratory methods in primatology: A practical guide* (pp. 122–139). Cambridge University Press.

Annett, M. 1987. Handedness as chance or as species characteristic. *Behavioral and Brain Sciences, 10*(2), 263–264.

ASP (Am. Soc. Primatol.). 2000. ASP policy statement on protecting the health of wild primates. American Society of Primatologists. https://www.asp.org/society/resolutions/primate_health.cfm.

ASP (Am. Soc. Primatol.). 2001. ASP policy statement on the ethical treatment of nonhuman primates. American Society of Primatologists. https://www.asp.org/society/resolutions/EthicalTreatmentOfNonHumanPrimates.cfm.

ASP (Am. Soc. Primatol.). 2014. Code of best practices in field primatology. American Society of Primatologists. https://www.asp.org/society/resolutions/bestpractices.cfm.

Asquith, P. 1986. Anthropomorphism and the Japanese and Western traditions in primatology. In J. G. Else and P. C. Lee (Eds.), *Primate ontogeny, cognition and social behaviour: Proceedings of the 10th Congress of the International Primatological Society Vol. 3.* (pp. 61–71). Cambridge University Press.

Asquith, P. 1997. Why anthropomorphism is not metaphor: Crossing concepts and cultures in animal behavior studies. In R. W. Mitchell, N. S. Thompson, and H. Lyn Miles (Eds.), *Anthropomorphism, anecdotes, and animals* (pp. 21–34). State University of New York Press.

Bahr, N. I., Palme, R., Möhle, U., Hodges, J. K., and Heistermann, M. 2000. Comparative aspects of the metabolism and excretion of cortisol in three individual nonhuman primates. *General and Comparative Endocrinology, 117*(3), 427–438.

Bakeman, R., and Gottman, J. M. 1997. *Observing interaction: An introduction to sequential analysis* (2nd. ed.). Cambridge University Press.

Barrickman, N. L., Schreier, A. L., and Glander, K. E. 2015. Testing parallel laser image scaling for remotely measuring body dimensions on mantled howling monkeys (*Alouatta palliata*). *American Journal of Primatology, 77*(8), 823–832.

Baulu, J., and Redmond Jr., D. E. 1978. Some sampling considerations in the quantitation of monkey behavior under field and captive conditions. *Primates, 19*(2), 391–400.

Beattie, G. W., and Beattie, C. A. 1981. Postural congruence in a naturalistic setting. *Semiotica, 35*(1/2), 41–55.

Behringer V., and Deschner, T. 2017. Non-invasive monitoring of physiological markers in primates. *Hormones and Behavior, 91*, 3–18.

Berg, W., Jolly, A., Rambeloarivony, H., Andrianome, V., and Rasamimanana, H. 2009. A scoring system for coat and tail condition in ringtailed lemurs, *Lemur catta*. *American Journal of Primatology, 71*(3), 183–190.

Bernstein, I. S. 1991. An empirical comparison of focal and ad libitum scoring with commentary on instantaneous scans, all occurrence and one-zero techniques. *Animal Behavior, 42*(5), 721–728.

Blekhman, R., Tang, K., Archie, E. A., Barreiro, L. B., Johnson, Z. P., Wilson, M. E., John, J., Yuan, M. L., Gesquiere, L., Grieneisen, L. E., and Tung, J. 2016. Common methods for fecal sample storage in field studies yield consistent signatures of individual identity in microbiome sequencing data. *Scientific Reports, 6*, 31519.

Bolker, B. M, Brooks, M. E., Clark, C. J., Geange, S. W., Poulsen, J. R., Stevens, M. H. H., and White, J. S. S. 2009. Generalized linear mixed models: A practical guide for ecology and evolution. *Trends in Ecology and Evolution, 24*(3), 127–135.

Box, H. 1984. *Primate behaviour and social ecology.* Chapman and Hall.

Boyd, H. L. 1998. *Postural congruence in a captive group of Tonkean macaques* (*Macaca tonkeana*). MA Thesis in Anthropology, University of Calgary.

Boyle, S. A., Lourenço, W. C., Da Silva, L. R., and Smith, A. T. 2009. Home range estimates vary with sample size and methods. *Folia Primatologica, 80*(1), 33–42.

Brent, L. J. N., Lehmann, J., and Ramos-Fernández, G. 2011. Social network analysis in the study of nonhuman primates: A historical perspective. *American Journal of Primatology, 73*(8), 720–730.

Brett, F. L., Turner, T. R., Jolly, C. J., and Cauble, R. G. 1982. Trapping baboons and vervet monkeys from wild, free-ranging populations. *The Journal of Wildlife Management, 46*(1), 164–174.

Brim, J. A., and Spain, D. H. 1974. *Research design in anthropology: Paradigms and pragmatics in the testing of hypotheses.* Holt, Rinehart & Winston.

Carpenter, C. R. 1934. A field study of the behavior and social relations of howling monkeys (*Alouatta palliata*). *Comparative Psychology Monographs, 10*(48), 1–168.

Carpenter, C. R. 1940. A field study in Siam of the behavior and social relations of the gibbon (*Hylobates lar*). *Comparative Psychology Monographs, 16*(5), 1–212.

Castro-Arellano, I., Madrid-Luna, C., Lacher Jr., T. E., and León-Paniagua, L. 2010. Hair-trap efficacy for detecting mammalian carnivores in the tropics. *The Journal of Wildlife Management, 72*(6), 1405–1412.

Centers for Disease Control and Prevention. 2009. *Biosafety in microbiological and biomedical laboratories* (5th ed.). U.S. Department of Health and Human Services.

Chapman, C. A., Wrangham, R., and Chapman, L. J. 1994. Indices of habitat-wide fruit abundance in tropical forests. *Biotropica, 26*(2), 160–171.

Clayton, J. B., Gomez, A., Amato, K., Knights, D., Travis, D. A., Blekhman, R., Knight, R., Leigh, S., Stumpf, R., Wolf, T., Glander, K. E., Cabana, F., and Johnson, T. J. 2018. The gut microbiome of nonhuman primates: Lessons in ecology and evolution. *American Journal of Primatology, 80*(6), e22867.

Coelho Jr., A. M., and Bramblett, C. A. 1990. Behaviour of the genus *Papio*: Ethogram, taxonomy, methods and comparative measures. In P. K. Seth and S. Seth (Eds.), *Perspectives in primate biology, Vol. 3* (pp. 117–140). Today and Tomorrow's Printers and Publishers.

Coleing, A. 2009. The application of social network theory to animal behaviour. *Bioscience Horizons, 2*(1), 32–43.

Colwell, R. K. 1974. Predictability, constancy, and contingency of periodic phenomena. *Ecology, 55*(5), 1148–1153.

Cords, M. 1993. On operationally defining reconciliation. *American Journal of Primatology, 29*(4), 255–268.

Council, S. E., Savage, A. M., Urban, J. M., Ehlers, M. E., Pate Skene, J. H., Platt, M. L., Dunn, R. R. and Horvath, J. E. 2016. Diversity and evolution of the primate skin microbiome. *Proceedings of the Royal Society B, 283*(1922), 20152586.

Cristóbal-Azkarate, J., Maréchal, L., Semple, S., Majolo, B., and MacLarnon, A. 2016. Metabolic strategies in wild male Barbary macaques: Evidence from faecal measurement of thyroid hormone. *Biology Letters, 12*(4), 20160168.

Crockford, C., Wittig, R. M., Langergraber, K., Ziegler, T. E., Zuberbühler, K., and Deschner, T. 2013. Urinary oxytocin and social bonding in related and unrelated wild chimpanzees. *Proceedings of the Royal Society B: Biological Sciences, 280*(1755), 20122765.

Czekala, N. M., and Callison, L. 1996. Pregnancy diagnosis in the black rhinoceros (*Diceros bicornis*) by salivary hormone analysis. *Zoo Biology, 15*(1), 37–44.

Darwin, C. 1872. *The expression of the emotions in man and animals.* University of Chicago Press (reprint 1965).

Defler, T. R. 1995. The time budget of a group of wild woolly monkeys (*Lagothris lagotricha*). *International Journal of Primatology, 16*(1), 107–120.

de Lampe, M. G., Bergeron, Y., McNeil, R., and Leduc, A. 1992. Seasonal flowering and fruiting patterns in tropical semi-arid vegetation of Northeastern Venezuela. *Biotropica, 24*(1), 64–72.

Delgado, R. R., and Delgado, J. M. R. 1962. An objective approach to measurement of behavior. *Philosophy of Science, 29*(3), 253–268.

De Vleeschouwer, K., van Elsacker, L., and Verheyen, R. F. 1995. Effect of posture on hand preferences during experimental food reaching in bonobos (*Pan paniscus*). *Journal of Comparative Psychology, 109*, 203–307.

DeVore, I., and Washburn, S. L. 1963. Baboon ecology and human evolution. In F. C. Howell and F. Bourliere (Eds.), *African ecology and human evolution* (pp. 335–367). Aldine/Atherton Publishers.

de Waal, F. B. M., and van Roosmalen, A. 1979. Reconciliation and consolation among chimpanzees. *Behavioral Ecology and Sociobiology, 5*, 55–66.

Di Fiore, A. 2003. Molecular genetic approaches to the study of primate behavior, social organization, and reproduction. *American Journal of Physical Anthropology, 122*(537), 62–99.

Di Fiore, A., and Rendall, D. 1994. Evolution of social organization: A reappraisal for primates by using phylogenetic methods. *Proceedings of the National Academy of Sciences of the USA, 91*(21), 9941–9945.

DiGiano, L., Nagle, C. A., Quiroga, S., Paul, N., Farinati, Z., Torres, M., and Mendizabal, A. F. 1992. Salivary progesterone for the assessment of the ovarian function in the capuchin monkey (*Cebus apella*). *International Journal of Primatology, 13*(2), 113–123.

Doyle, G. S. 2010. *Where there is no doctor: Preventive and emergency healthcare in uncertain times.* Process Self-Reliance Series.

Dunbar, R. I., Korstjens, A. H., and Lehmann, J. 2009. Time as an ecological constraint. *Biological Reviews, 84*(3), 413–429.

Emery Thompson, M., and Knott, C. D. 2008. Urinary C-peptide of insulin as a non-invasive marker of energy balance in wild orangutans. *Hormones and Behavior, 53*(4), 526–535.

Engh, A. L., Hoffmeier, R. R., Cheney, D. L., and Seyfarth, R. M., 2006. Who, me? Can baboons infer the target of vocalizations? *Animal Behaviour, 71*(2), 381–387.

Fedigan, L. M. (2010). Ethical issues faced by field primatologists: Asking the relevant questions. *American Journal of Primatology, 72*(9), 754–771.

Fourie, N. H., and Bernstein, R. M. 2011. Hair cortisol levels track phylogenetic and age related differences in hypothalamic–pituitary–adrenal (HPA) axis activity in non-human primates. *General and Comparative Endocrinology, 174*(2), 150–155.

Frankie, G. W., Baker, H. G., and Opler, P. A. 1974. Comparative phenological studies of trees in tropical wet and dry forests in the lowlands of Costa Rica. *Journal of Ecology, 62*(3), 881–913.

Fujita, S., Mitsunaga, F., Sugiura, H., and Shimizu, K. 2001. Measurement of urinary and fecal steroid metabolites during the ovarian cycle in captive and wild Japanese macaques, *Macaca fuscata. American Journal of Primatology, 53*(4), 167–176.

Gagneux, P., Boesch, C., and Woodruff, D. S. 1997. Microsatellite scoring errors associated with noninvasive genotyping based on nuclear DNA amplified from shed hair. *Molecular Ecology, 6*(9), 861–868.

Gamble, H., Alvin, R., Gajadhar, A., and Solomon, M. B. 1996. Methods for the detection of trichinellosis in horses. *Journal of Food Protection, 59*(4), 420–425.

Gamble, H. R., Pozio, E., Bruschi, F., Nöckler, K., Kapel, C. M. O., and Gajadhar, A. A. 2004. International Commission on Trichinellosis: Recommendations on the use of serological tests for the detection of *Trichinella* infection in animals and man. *Parasite, 11*(1), 3–13.

Ganzhorn, J. U., Rakotondranary, S. J., and Ratovonamana, Y. R. 2011. Habitat description and phenology. In J. M. Setchell and D. J. Curtis (Eds.), *Field and laboratory methods in primatology: A practical guide* (2nd ed.) (pp. 51–68). Cambridge University Press.

Gillespie, T. R. 2006. Noninvasive assessment of gastrointestinal parasite infections in free-ranging primates. *International Journal of Primatology, 27*(4), 1129–1143.

Glander, K. E. 1993. Capture and marking techniques for arboreal primates. In A. Estrada, E. Rodriguez-Luna, R. Lopez-Wilchis, and R. Coates-Estrada (Eds.), *Estudios primatologicos en Mexico, Vol. 1* (pp. 299–304). Universidad Veracruzana.

Glander, K. E., Fedigan, L. M., Fedigan, L., and Chapman, C. 1991. Field methods for capture and measurement of three monkey species in Costa Rica. *Folia Primatologica 57*, 70–82.

Glander, K. E., Wright, P. C., Daniels, P. S., and Merenlender, A. M. 1992. Morphometrics and testicle size of rain forest lemur species from southeastern Madagascar. *Journal of Human Evolution, 22*(1), 1–17.

Goossens, B., Anthony, N., Jeffery, K., Johnson-Bawe, M., and Bruford, M. W. 2003. Collection, storage and analysis of non-invasive genetic material in primate biology. In J. M. Setchell and D. J. Curtis (Eds.), *Field and laboratory methods in primatology: A practical guide* (pp. 295–308). Cambridge University Press.

Groves, C., and Harding, J. 2003. Morphology, morphometrics and taxonomy. In J. M. Setchell and D. J. Curtis (Eds.), *Field and laboratory methods in primatology: A practical guide* (pp. 140–157). Cambridge University Press.

Grueter, C. C., Li, D., Ren, B., and Wei, F. 2009. Choice of analytical method can have dramatic effects on primate home range estimates. *Primates, 50*(1), 81.

Gumert, M. D. 2007. Grooming and infant handling interchange in *Macaca fascicularis*: The relationship between infant supply and grooming payment. *International Journal of Primatology, 28*(5), 1059–1074.

Hailman, J. P., and Strier, K. B. 1997. *Planning, proposing, and presenting science effectively.* Cambridge University Press.

Hayne, D. W. 1949. Calculation of size of home range. *Journal of Mammalogy, 30*(1), 1–18.

Heistermann, M. 2010. Non-invasive monitoring of endocrine status in laboratory primates: Methods, guidelines and applications. *Advances in Science and Research, 5*(1), 1–9.

Heistermann, M., and Hodges, J. K. 1995. Endocrine monitoring of the ovarian cycle and pregnancy in the saddle-back tamarin (*Saguinus fuscicollis*) by measurement of steroid conjugates in urine. *American Journal of Primatology, 35*(2), 117–127.

Heistermann, M., Tari, S., and Hodges, J. K. 1993. Measurement of faecal steroids for monitoring ovarian function in New World primates, Callitrichidae. *Reproduction, 99*(1), 243–251.

Henderson, P. A. 2003. *Practical methods in ecology.* Blackwell Science.

Heymsfield, S. B., Arteaga, C., McManus, C., Smith, J., and Moffitt, S. 1983. Measurement of muscle mass in humans: Validity of the 24-hour urinary creatinine method. *The American Journal of Clinical Nutrition, 37*(3), 478–494.

Higham, J. P. 2016. Field endocrinology of nonhuman primates: Past, present, and future. *Hormones and Behavior, 84*, 145–155.

Higham, J. P., Vitale, A. B., Rivera, A. M., Ayala, J. E., and Maestripieri, D. 2010. Measuring salivary analytes from free-ranging monkeys. *Physiology and Behavior, 101*(5), 601–607.

Hinde, R. A. 1973. On the design of check sheets. *Primates, 14*(4), 393–406.

Hinde, R. A. 1976. Interactions, relationships and social structure. *Man, 11*(1), 1–17.

Hinde, R. A., and Atkinson, S. 1970. Assessing the roles of social partners in maintaining mutual proximity, as exemplified by mother-infant relations in rhesus monkeys. *Animal Behaviour, 18*(1), 169–176.

Hodges, J. K., Czekala, N. M., and Lasley, B. L. 1979. Estrogen and luteinizing hormone secretion in diverse primate species from simplified urinary analysis. *Journal of Medical Primatology, 8*, 349–364.

Hodges, J. K., and Eastman, S. A. K. 1984. Monitoring ovarian function in marmosets and tamarins by the measurement of urinary estrogen metabolites. *American Journal of Primatology, 6*(3), 187–197.

Hodges, J. K., and Heistermann, M. 2003. Field endocrinology: Monitoring hormonal changes in free-ranging primates. In J. M. Setchell and D. J. Curtis (Eds.), *Field and laboratory methods in primatology: A practical guide* (pp. 282–294). Cambridge University Press.

Hopkins, W. D. 1999. On the other hand: Statistical issues in the assessment and interpretation of hand preference data in nonhuman primates. *International Journal of Primatology, 20*(6), 851–866.

Hughes, K. 2003. The Global Positioning System, Geographical Information Systems and remote sensing. In J. M. Setchell and D. J. Curtis (Eds.), *Field and laboratory methods in primatology* (pp. 57–73). Cambridge University Press.

Jazrawi, S. E. 2000. *Postural congruence in a captive group of chimpanzees (Pan troglodytes).* Master's Thesis, University of Calgary.

Jeanpierre, M. 1987. A rapid method for the purification of DNA from blood. *Nucleic Acids Research, 15*(22), 9611.

Johnson, S. M., and Bolstad, O. D. 1973. Methodological issues in naturalistic observation: Some problems and solutions for field research. In L. A. Hamerlynch, L. C. Handy, and E. J. Mash (Eds.), *Behavior change: Methodology, concepts, and practice* (pp. 7–67). Research Press.

Jolly, C. J., Phillips-Conroy, J. E., and Müller, A. E. 2011. Trapping primates. In J. M. Setchell and D. J. Curtis (Eds.), *Field and laboratory methods in primatology: A practical guide* (2nd ed.) (pp. 133–145). Cambridge University Press.

Kappeler, P. M., and van Schaik, C. P. 1992. Methodological and evolutionary aspects of reconciliation among primates. *Ethology, 92*(1), 51–69.

Kappeler, P. M., and van Schaik, C. P. 2002. Evolution of primate social systems. *International Journal of Primatology, 23*(4), 707–740.

Kappeler, P. M., and Watts, D. P. 2012. *Long-term field studies of primates.* Springer Science and Business Media.

Kasper, C., and Voelkl, B. 2009. A social network analysis of primate groups. *Primates, 50*(4), 343–356.

Kays, R., Crofoot, M. C., Jetz, W., and Wikelski, M. 2015. Terrestrial animal tracking as an eye of life and planet. *Science, 348*(6240), aaa2478.

Kennedy, J. S. 1992. *The new anthropomorphism.* Cambridge University Press.

King, S. J., Morelli, T. L., Arrigo-Nelson, S., Ratelolahy, F. J., Godfrey, L. R., Wyatt, J., Tecot, S., Jernvall, J., and Wright, P. C. 2011. Morphometrics and pattern of growth in wild sifakas (*Propithecus edwardsi*) at Ranomafana National Park, Madagascar. *American Journal of Primatology, 73*(2), 155–172.

Kirschbaum, C., and Hellhammer, D. H. 1989. Salivary cortisol in psychobiological research: An overview. *Neuropsychobiology, 22*(3), 150–169.

Köhler, W. 1925. *The mentality of apes.* Harcourt, Brace & Co.

Kraemer, H. C. 1979. One-zero sampling in the study of primate behaviour. *Primates, 20,* 237–244.

Kramer, K. M., Cushing, B. S., Carter, C. S., Wu, J., and Ottinger, M. A. 2004. Sex and species differences in plasma oxytocin using an enzyme immunoassay. *Canadian Journal of Zoology, 82*(8), 1194–1200.

Krebs, C. J. 1999. *Ecological methodology* (2nd ed). Addison Wesley Longman.

Krebs, H. A. 1975. The August Krogh principle: "For many problems there is an animal on which it can be most conveniently studied." *Journal of Experimental Zoology, 194*(1), 221–226.

Kurup, G. U., and Kumar, A. 1993. Time budget and activity patterns of the lion-tailed macaque. *International Journal of Primatology, 14*(1), 27–40.

Larsen, R. S., Moresco, A., and Glander, K. E. 1999. Field anesthesia and capture techniques of free-ranging mantled howling monkeys (*Alouatta palliata*) in Costa Rica. *Proceedings of the American Association of Zoo Veterinarians,* 243–247.

Lehner, P. N. 1996. *Handbook of ethological methods* (2nd ed.). Cambridge University Press.

Lonsdorf, E. V., and Hopkins, W. D. 2005. Wild chimpanzees show population-level handedness for tool use. *Proceedings of the National Academy of Sciences, 102*(35), 12634–12638.

Loy, J. D., and Peters, C. B. 1991. *Understanding behavior: What primate studies tell us about human behavior.* Oxford University Press.

MacKinnon, K. C., and Riley, E. P. 2010. Field primatology of today: Current ethical issues. *American Journal of Primatology, 72,* 749–753.

Makagon, M. M., McCowan, B., and Mench, J. A. 2012. How can social network analysis contribute to social behavior research in applied ethology? *Applied Animal Behaviour Science, 138*(3–4), 152–161.

Marriner, L. M., and Drickamer, L. C. 1994. Factors influencing stereotyped behavior of primates in a zoo. *Zoo Biology, 13*(3), 267–275.

Martin, P., and Bateson, P. 2007. *Measuring behaviour: An introductory guide* (3rd ed.). Cambridge University Press.

Mason, V. C., Li, G., Minx, P., Schmitz, J., Churakov, G., Doronina, L., et al., and Murphy, W. J. 2016. Genomic analysis reveals hidden biodiversity within colugos, the sister group to primates. *Science Advances, 2*(8), 1–15.

McCann, C., Buchanan-Smith, H., Farmer, K., Fitch-Snyder, H., Jones-Engel, L., Prescott, M., and Taylor, S. 2007. *IPS international guidelines for the acquisition, care and breeding of nonhuman primates* (2nd ed.). International Primatological Society.

McCulloch, C. E., and Searle, S. R. 2001. *Generalized, linear, and mixed models.* John Wiley & Sons.

McCullough, M. E., Smith Churchland, P., and Mendez, A. J. 2013. Problems with measuring peripheral oxytocin: Can the data on oxytocin and human behavior be trusted? *Neuroscience and Biobehavioral Reviews, 37*(8), 1485–1492.

McDonald, J. H. 2014. *Handbook of biological statistics* (3rd ed.). Sparky House Publishing.

Melin, A. D., Webb, S., Williamson, R., and Chiou, K. 2018. Data collection in field primatology: A renewed look at measuring foraging behaviour. In U. Kalbitzer and K. M. Jack (Eds.), *Primate life histories, sex roles, and adaptability—Essays in honour of Linda M. Fedigan* (pp. 161–192). Springer.

Menon, S., and Poirier, F. E. 1996. Lion-tailed macaques in a disturbed forest fragment: Activity patterns and time budget. *International Journal of Primatology, 17*(6), 969–986.

Mikula, P., Šaffa, G., Nelson, E., and Tryjanowski, P. 2018. Risk perception of vervet monkeys *Chlorocebus pygerythrus* to humans in urban and rural environments. *Behavioural Processes, 147*, 21–27.

Mitchell, R. W., Thompson, N. S., and Miles, H. L. (Eds.). 1997. *Anthropomorphism, anecdotes, and animals.* State University of New York Press.

Möhle, U., Heistermann, M., Palme, R., and Hodges, J. K. 2002. Characterization of urinary and fecal metabolites of testosterone and their measurement for assessing gonadal endocrine function in male nonhuman primates. *General and Comparative Endocrinology, 129*(3), 135–145.

Mori, A. 1979. Analysis of population changes by measurement of body weight in the Koshima troop of Japanese monkeys. *Primates, 20*(3), 371–397.

Morin, P. A., Chambers, K. E., Boesch, C., and Vigilant, L. 2001. Quantitative polymerase chain reaction analysis of DNA from noninvasive samples for accurate microsatellite genotyping of wild chimpanzees (*Pan troglodytes verus*). *Molecular Ecology, 10*(7), 1835–1844.

Morisita, M. 1959. Measuring of interspecific association and similarity between communities. *Memoirs of the Faculty of Science Kyushu University Series E, 3*, 65–80.

Morisita, M. 1962. Id-index, a measure of dispersion of individuals. *Researches in Population Ecology, 4*(1), 1–7.

Munson, L., Karesh, W. B., McEntee, M. F., Lowenstine, L. J., Roelke-Parker, M. E., Williams, E., and Woodford, M. H. 2006. *Necropsy of wild animals.* Wildlife Conservation Society.

National Research Council (NRC). 1981. *Techniques for the study of primate population ecology.* National Academy Press.

Odum, E. P., and Kuenzler, E. J. 1955. Measurement of territory and home range size in birds. *Auk, 72*(2), 128–137.

Oxnard, C. E. 1983. *The order of man.* Yale University Press and Hong Kong University Press.

Paterson, J. D. 1992. An alternative view: Behaviour as a multi-causal strategy for survival. In F. D. Burton (Ed.), *Social processes and mental abilities in non-human primates: Evidences from longitudinal field studies* (pp. 129–182). Edwin Mellen Press.

Perry, G. H., Marioni, J. C., Melsted, P., and Gilad, Y. 2010. Genomic-scale capture and sequencing of endogenous DNA from feces. *Molecular Ecology, 19*(24), 5332–5344.

Persson, T., Sauciuc, G. A., and Madsen, E. A. 2018. Spontaneous cross-species imitation in interactions between chimpanzees and zoo visitors. *Primates, 59*(1), 19–29.

Poindexter, S. A., Reinhardt, K. D., Nijman, V., and Nekaris, K. A. I. 2018. Slow lorises (*Nycticebus* spp.) display evidence of handedness in the wild and in captivity. *Laterality: Asymmetries of Body, Brain and Cognition, 23*(6), 705–721.

Prieur, J., Lemasson, A., Barbu, S., and Blois-Heulin, C. 2019. History, development and current advances concerning the evolutionary roots of human right-handedness and language: Brain lateralisation and manual laterality in nonhuman primates. *Ethology, 125*(1), 1–28.

Prugnolle, F., Durand, P., Neel, C., Ollomo, B., Ayala, F. J., Arnathau, C., et al., and Renault, F. 2010. African great apes are natural hosts of multiple related malaria species, including *Plasmodium falciparum*. *Proceedings of the National Academy of Sciences, 107*(4), 1458–1463.

Pusey, A. E., Oehlert, G. W., Williams, J. M., and Goodall, J. 2005. Influence of ecological and social factors on body mass of wild chimpanzees. *International Journal of Primatology, 26*(1), 3–31.

Rees, P. A. 2015. *Studying captive animals: A workbook of methods in behaviour, welfare and ecology.* John Wiley & Sons.

Rendall, D., & Di Fiore, A. (1995). The road less traveled: Phylogenetic perspectives in primatology. *Evolutionary Anthropology: Issues, News, and Reviews, 4*(2), 43–52.

Rhine, R. J., and Ender, P. B. 1983. Comparability of methods used in the sampling of primate behavior. *American Journal of Primatology, 5*(1), 1–15.

Rhine, R. J., and Flanigan, M. 1978. An empirical comparison of one-zero, focal animal and instantaneous methods of sampling spontaneous primate social behavior. *Primates, 42*(5), 353–361.

Rhine, R. J., and Linville, A. K. 1980. Properties of one-zero scores in observational studies of primate social behavior: The effect of assumption on empirical analyses. *Primates, 21*, 111–122.

Rhine, R. J., Norton, G. W., Wynn, G. M., and Wynn, R. D. 1985. Weaning of free-ranging infant baboons (*Papio cynocephalus*) as indicated by one-zero and instantaneous sampling of feeding. *International Journal of Primatology, 6*, 491–499.

Riley, E. P., and Bezanson, M. 2018. Ethics of primate fieldwork: Toward an ethically engaged primatology. *Annual Review of Anthropology, 47*, 493–512.

Rinaldi, S., Déchaud, H., Biessy, C., Morin-Raverot, V., Toniolo, P., Zeleniuch-Jacquotte, A., et al., and Kaaks, R. 2001. Reliability and validity of commercially available, direct radioimmunoassays for measurement of blood androgens and estrogens in postmenopausal women. *Cancer Epidemiology and Prevention Biomarkers, 10*(7), 757–765.

Robbins, M. M., and Czekala, N. M. 1997. A preliminary investigation of urinary testosterone and cortisol levels in wild male mountain gorillas. *American Journal of Primatology, 43*(1), 51–64.

Rogers, L. J. 2018. Manual bias, behavior, and cognition in common marmosets and other primates. *Progress in Brain Research, 238*, 91–113.

Rothman, J. M., Chapman, C. A., Twinomugisha, D., Wasserman, M. D., Lambert, J. E., and Goldberg, T. L. 2008. Measuring physical traits of primates remotely: The use of parallel lasers. *American Journal of Primatology, 70*(12), 1191–1195.

Rothman, J. M., Chapman, C. A., and Van Soest, P. J. 2012. Methods in primate nutritional ecology: A user's guide. *International Journal of Primatology, 33*, 542–566.

Russell, W. M. S., and Burch, R. L. 1959. *The principles of humane experimental technique.* Methuen.

Sapolsky, R. M. 1982. The endocrine stress-response and social status in the wild baboon. *Hormones and Behavior, 16*(3), 279–292.

Sapolsky, R. M. 1986. Stress-induced elevation of testosterone concentrations in high ranking baboons: Role of catecholamines. *Endocrinology, 118*(4), 1630–1635.

Sauciuc, G. A., Persson, T., and Madsen, E. 2017. The social side of imitation in human evolution and development: Shared intentionality and imitation games in chimpanzees and 6-month old infants. In A. Arweström Jansson (Ed.), *Proceedings of the 13th Swecog Conference* (pp. 21–23). Uppsala University.

Scheflen, A. E. 1964. The significance of posture in communication systems. *Psychiatry: Journal for the Study of Interpersonal Processes, 27*(4), 316–331.

Scheflen, A. E. 1965. Quasi-courtship behavior in psychotherapy. *Psychiatry: Journal for the Study of Interpersonal Processes, 28*(3), 245–257.

Scheflen, A. E. 1972. *Body language and social order: Communication as behavioral control.* Prentice Hall.

Scott, J., and Stokman, F. N. 2015. Social networks. In J. D. Scott (Ed.), *International encyclopedia of the social and behavioral sciences* (2nd ed.) (pp. 473–477). Elsevier Ltd.

Setchell, J. M., and Curtis, D. J. (Eds.). 2011. *Field and laboratory methods in primatology: A practical guide* (2nd ed.). Cambridge University Press.

Seuer, C., Jacobs, A., Amblard, F., Petit, O., and King, A. J. 2011. How can social network analysis improve the study of primate behavior? *American Journal of Primatology, 71*, 1–17.

Shideler, S. E., Ortuno, A. M., Moran, F. M., Moorman, E. A., and Lasley, B. L. 1993. Simple extraction and enzyme immunoassays for estrogen and progesterone metabolites in the feces of *Macaca fascicularis* during non-conceptive and conceptive ovarian cycles. *Biology of Reproduction, 48*(6), 1290–1298.

Shirtcliff, E. A., Granger, D. A., and Likos, A. 2002. Gender differences in the validity of testosterone measured in saliva by immunoassay. *Hormones and Behavior, 42*(1), 62–69.

Siegel, S. and Castellan Jr., N. J. 1988. *Nonparametric statistics for the behavioral sciences.* McGraw-Hill.

Silk, J. B. 1997. The function of peaceful post-conflict contacts among primates. *Primates, 38*(3), 265–280.

Sillen-Tullberg, B., and Møller, A. P. 1993. The relationship between concealed ovulation and mating systems in anthropoid primates: A phylogenetic analysis. *American Naturalist, 14*(1), 1–25.

Snowdon, C. T., and Ziegler, T. E. 2015. Variation in prolactin is related to variation in sexual behavior and contact affiliation. *PLoS ONE, 10*(3), e0120650.

Soltis, J., Wegner, F. H., and Newman, J. D. 2005. Urinary prolactin is correlated with mothering and allo-mothering in squirrel monkeys. *Physiology & Behavior, 84*(2), 295–301.

Southwood, T. R. E., and Henderson, P. A. 2000. *Ecological methods* (3rd ed.). Blackwell Science.

Spellerberg, I. F. 1991. *Monitoring ecological change.* Cambridge University Press.

Stearns, S. C. 1981. On measuring fluctuating environments: Predictability, constancy, and contingency. *Ecology, 62*(1), 185–199.

Tabachnick, B. G., and Fidell, L. S. 2007. *Using multivariate statistics.* Allyn & Bacon, Pearson Education.

Teichroeb, J. A., Saj, T. L., Paterson, J. D., and Sicotte, P. 2003. Effect of group size on activity budgets of *Colobus vellerosus* in Ghana. *International Journal of Primatology, 24*(4), 743–758.

Teichroeb, J. A., and Sicotte, P. 2008. Social correlates of fecal testosterone in male ursine colobus monkeys (*Colobus vellerosus*): The effect of male reproductive competition in seasonal breeders. *Hormones and Behavior, 54*(3), 417–423.

Teichroeb, J. A., and Sicotte, P. 2009. Test of the ecological-constraints model on ursine colobus monkeys (*Colobus vellerosus*) in Ghana. *American Journal of Primatology, 71*(1), 49–59.

Teichroeb, J. A., Stead, S. M., Edwards, P. D., Landry F., Palme, R., and Boonstra, R. 2020. Anogenital distance as an indicator of competitive ability in Rwenzori Angolan colobus. *American Journal of Primatology, 82*(3), e23111.

Tinbergen, N. 1963. On aims and methods of ethology. *Zeitschrift für Tierpsychologie, 20*, 410–433.

Touma, C., Sachser, N., Möstl, E., and Palme, R. 2003. Effects of sex and time of day on metabolism and excretion of corticosterone in urine and feces of mice. *General and Comparative Endocrinology, 130*(3), 267–278.

Turpeinen, U., and Hämäläinen, E. 2013. Determination of cortisol in serum, saliva and urine. *Best Practice and Research, Clinical Endocrinology and Metabolism, 27*(6), 795–801.

Uehara, S., and Nishida, T. 1987. Body weights of wild chimpanzees (*Pan troglodytes schweinfurthii*) of the Mahale Mountains National Park, Tanzania. *American Journal of Physical Anthropology, 72*(3), 315–321.

Unwin, S., Ancrenaz, M., and Bailey, W. 2011. Handling, anaesthesia, health evaluation and biological sampling. In J. M. Setchell and D. J. Curtis (Eds.), *Field and laboratory methods in primatology: A practical guide* (2nd ed.) (pp. 147–168). Cambridge University Press.

Valderrama, X., Karesh, W. B., Wildman, D. E., and Melnick, D. J. 1999. Noninvasive methods for collecting fresh hair tissue. *Molecular Ecology, 8*(10), 1749–1750.

van Hooff, J. A. R. A. M. 1967. The facial displays of the catarrhine monkeys and apes. In D. Morris (Ed.), *Primate ethology* (pp. 7–68). Weidenfeld and Nicolson.

Vining, R. F., and McGinley, R. A. 1986. Hormones in saliva. *CRC Critical Reviews in Clinical Laboratory Sciences, 23*(2), 95–146.

Washburn, S. L., Jay, P. C., and Lancaster, J. B. (1965). Field studies of Old World monkeys and apes. *Science, 150*(3703), 1541–1547.

Watanabe, G., Nozaki, M., Taya, K., Katakai, Y., and Sasamoto, S. 1990. Immunoreactive inhibin levels in peripheral blood during the breeding season in the female Japanese monkey. *Biology of Reproduction, 43*(2), 196–201.

Whitehead, H. 2008. *Analyzing animal societies: Quantitative methods for vertebrate social analysis*. University of Chicago Press.

Wilson, E. O. 1975. *Sociobiology*. Harvard University Press.

Wiseman, J. 2014. *The SAS survival handbook: The ultimate guide to surviving anywhere* (3rd ed.). Harper Collins.

Wolfe, N. D., Karesh, W. B., Kilbourn, A. M., Cox-Singh, J., Bosi, E. J., Rahman, H. A., Tassy Prosser, A., Singh, B., Andau, M., and Spielman, A. 2002. The impact of ecological conditions on the prevalence of malaria among orangutans. *Vector Borne and Zoonotic Diseases, 2*(2), 97–103.

Worton, B. J. 1989. Kernel methods for estimating the utilization distribution in home-range studies. *Ecology, 70*(1), 164–168.

Ziegler, T. E, and Crockford, C. 2017. Neuroendocrine control in social relationships in non-human primates: Field based evidence. *Hormones and Behavior, 91*, 107–121.

Zuckerman, S. 1932. *The social life of monkeys and apes*. Harcourt Brace.